Diana Richmond comes from a Scottish émigré family living in London, and was educated at Downe House and various L.C.C. Art Schools. After a job in music publishing, she married the brother of a schoolfriend who had awakened her interest in Egypt and Palestine. Separated for five years during World War Two, she rejoined her husband in Jerusalem; but British rule was already crumbling, and in 1947 he entered the Foreign Service. Thereafter the author lived in Baghdad, 'Amman, Cairo, Kuwait and Khartoum. She has travelled in North Africa and Iran, crossed many deserts, and visited ancient sites. She is well-known as a supporter of the Palestinian cause, and has published articles in *The Catholic Herald, World Faiths,* and *Middle East International.*

A picture of 'Antar, from Damascus but first seen in Cairo, and soon afterwards at the home of 'Iraqi friends in Italy, inspired the research which has led to the retelling of these ancient tales.

'ANTAR AND 'ABLA
A Bedouin Romance

Rewritten and arranged by
DIANA RICHMOND
Illustrations by Ulrica Lloyd R.A.

QUARTET BOOKS

LONDON   MELBOURNE   NEW YORK

First published by Quartet Books Limited 1978
A member of the Namara Group
27 Goodge Street, London W1P 1FD

Copyright © 1978 by Diana Richmond

ISBN 0 7043 2162 9

Photoset by Red Lion Setters, Holborn, London
Printed in Great Britain at the Anchor Press Ltd,
and bound by Wm. Brendon & Son Ltd
both of Tiptree, Essex.

For Thomas

who was born in the capital of the Abbasids,
and who loves the Arabic-speaking world

'A good story-teller tries to make his
stories better every time he tells them'
— George MacDonald, *At the Back of the North Wind*

CONTENTS

ACKNOWLEDGEMENTS

The author would like to express her grateful thanks to Glubb Pasha, who helped meticulously with detail and transcription; and whose patient work and vast knowledge of the desert and its peoples have proved invaluable.

The episode of Ocab and Dahis, printed here as the third story, 'The Children of the Tribe', was first published in *Gazelle* magazine, and acknowledgement is made to Gazelle Publications, London, for their kind agreement to its being reprinted in this selection.

'ANTAR AND 'ABLA

AUTHOR'S NOTE

The sources that I have used in compiling this sequence of stories about 'Antar and 'Abla are listed below. To one who cannot read Arabic, Terrick Hamilton and Marcel Devic appear to have produced detailed and reliable translations. However, neither source offers the modern reader a version which remains faithful to the stories' cultural origins in the Arabic oral tradition. And although the third author, Gustave Rouger, with his gift of selection, threaded his way unerringly through a maze of material, he romanticized the tales in the European style; and finally digressed into Northern folklore to the extent of devising an early death for his 'Antar (who never married) in the manner not only of Baldur the Beautiful but also of El Cid. This is unacceptable since, in the original Arabic, the stories fill thirty-two volumes, in which 'Antar achieves a respected old age, and travels in both Europe and Africa before he dies.

I have, therefore, rewritten the stories entirely, and I have aimed at re-creating their original fluency, richness and chivalric pride.

The sources:

Antar, — a Bedoueen Romance, translated from the Arabic by Terrick Hamilton Esq (Oriental Secretary to the British Embassy at Constantinople), John Murray, London, 1819-20.

Les Aventures d'Antar, fils de Cheddad. Roman arabe des temps ante-Islamiques, translated by L. Marcel Devic, second edition, edited by E. Leroux for the Librairie de la Société Asiatique de l'école des langues orientales vivantes ..., Paris, 1878.

Le Roman d'Antar, tales selected and rewritten from Devic's versions by Gustave Rouger, H. Piazza, Paris, 1923.

INTRODUCTION

We in the West are very ignorant of any literature written in Arabic or in Arabia. Only if pressed might we remember *The Thousand and One Nights*, and although we would then recollect the world of Haroun ar Rashid, we might not know in which century to place him and his superb poets, nor would Baghdad or Mamluk Cairo seem very real to us. The tales, too, we would remember only as tales of magic and wealth, learning and sophistication.

Very different are the stories of 'Antar and 'Abla; they come from the real desert and the real wilderness, and they are told all over the Arabic-speaking world. Indeed, they have been told for some fourteen hundred years — at fairs and meetings and markets, around the camp-fires of camel-herds and soldiers, in coffee houses and at *chaikhanas*, and among children for generations.

These stories remained passed down by word of mouth for many years, and are supposed to have been written down eventually by Abdu' 'l Malik ibn Qurayb al Asmai' of Basrah, courtier to Haroun ar Rashid. They may be read nowadays in Arabic, and they comprise no less than thirty-two volumes in that form; but I have taken only a selection from one English source of 1819-20, and two French sources of the late nineteenth and early twentieth centuries (1878 and 1923). Though the three authors in question recognized the merits of these tales and the fascination of the history and events behind them, all three suffered from an underlying feeling of European

13

superiority, both towards the Bedouin and towards Islam (for though the stories are pre-Islamic, they are overlaid with Moslem characteristics). This is an attitude which I hope and believe we have now outgrown.

The stories of 'Antar are, some say, rated higher by the Arabs than are the tales in *The Thousand and One Nights*, perhaps because they encompass less fantasy. There is a reality about them, a down-to-earth, day-to-day validity supplementing the chivalry which is their theme. Some of the characters are real historical people, some of the situations authentic, and only the background to the stories needs explaining, since it differs so greatly from our own Western setting.

Far nearer to England than Greece is Arabic-speaking Morocco, yet we still know little of the history of this vast world of peoples who range from Agadir to Aden and beyond. We do not understand the families and tribes and nations which have, as a background to their lives and history, the harsh wilderness and desert, so different from the forests, lakes and grasslands of our northern world. In the time of the Great Arab conquests, during the triumphal onrush of Islam, the true and original believers were from the wilderness, but yet they were townsmen and merchants; and much of the interest of their emergence into the wealthy worlds of the Mediterranean and Persia lay in the fact that they were men far poorer and less worldly-wise than many of the ancient peoples they were to influence and conquer — peoples living upon highly cultivated soil and inhabiting highly civilized cities. The men of Mecca and Medina, and the merchants who organized this section of the trade routes from India and Africa and the Yemen to Greece and Rome, lived, as it were, on the coasts of a desert sea. This Arabian 'ocean' was nevertheless more accessible than we probably imagine. It was criss-crossed by established routes, its wells were known, armies and traders came and went on familiar tracks, guided by recognizable landmarks or the reliable stars.

Our stories are gathered from the period known as the 'time of Ignorance' before the birth of the Prophet, and our characters come from the desert dwellers of this Arabian 'ocean', those who despised the merchants and the town dwellers, and who were always on the move, seeking pasture for their goats, sheep and camels. 'Antar's own tribe ranged in hilly country some hundred miles north and west of Medina. The lives of these men, women and children were dependent upon the seasons, and they survived solely through their intimate knowledge of the forbidding desert — in danger of death from heat and cold alike, from flash floods in winter and from dust storms in summer. Isolated in the Hejaz, the Great Barrier, between the Nefood sand desert, the mountains and beyond these the coastal plain, they were yet part of a vast web of communication between Rome, Byzantium and Persia, Egypt, Abyssinia and the fertile and sophisticated Yemen.

These people existed in conditions too severe to admit of the amassing of much wealth, which could become a burden to them. Life, with its constant movement, left little time on their hands for the practice of religion, and even magic played a minor part in their world. They were realists, and only in language did they allow their imagination full rein. Together with all the peoples of Arabia, they had their long-established place of sanctuary at Mecca; they believed dimly in an afterlife, perhaps among the stars, and they had already conceived the idea of One God, though many lesser divinities, such as Lat and Uzza, still attracted their fear and worship. Meteorites could be the dwelling place of spirits from another world. Graves were marked by cairns, and offerings left there. The future might be divined by means of the flights of birds or arrows.

Tribal people, they admired, above all, courage, endurance, generosity and group loyalty. While immense individual freedom was treasured, total anarchy would plainly have rendered survival impossible, so there emerged among them a certain order and rule within the freedom; and a standard of honourable behaviour — to friend and foe alike — was set up as a general example. The raids, for instance, so frequently referred to in the stories of 'Antar, were not murderous in intent, but were for foraging and sustenance, the need arising from the sheer poverty of the bleak wilderness. Raids were also a means of displaying prowess and demonstrating skill and virility; it was not correct that men should wantonly be killed, since manslaughter carried severe penalties and led to blood-feuds which might last for generations.

The Bedouin, the camel-riders, were masters of the true desert. They could penetrate it further and ride over it faster than any others. They exacted tolls from the caravans frequenting it, and they would take tribute from the few sedentary families among them who might, in certain areas, settle down to the cultivation of dates in some fertile oasis; or from farmers who would till and crop the soil at the desert's edge. In this rough and mobile society, cohering through its own simple ordering of behaviour, one great form of artistic expression was paramount: the art of poetry and eloquence, the love of spoken words. The structure of their language was the Arabs' delight; the structure of each word could change like that of a child's 'cat's cradle' into as many varying shapes and meanings as these carefully manipulated string puzzles can assume when skilfully handled. Repartee and oratory were the gifts men and women longed for; and great contests of artistry were held at Ukaz. Here poems were delivered and remembered, and later written down, perhaps upon silk and in golden lettering. The finest of these would be suspended in honour within the Ka'aba at Mecca. The Arabian poets brought the desert to life for posterity and preserved their love for it in man's memory — preserved, too, their intense awareness of passion and love. The beginnings of their philosophy and their wonderings may be traced through their great endowment of poetry.

'Antar's poems were of such merit that he achieved the high honour of their suspension within the Ka'aba. His romantic story was the loom on which a web of stories has been woven, perhaps over centuries, and gaining much in the telling. In presenting a sequence of them here I have confined myself to those concerning two objectives. One is his legendary love for 'Abla. The other is his success in achieving his rightful position within the tribe — a matter of especial importance to the Bedouin since they held the idea that honour was in some way both inherited and capable of being passed on to a man's descendants. From these tales, I am convinced, the ancient story-tellers urge us to learn a lesson of magnanimity. Impressive as immense strength and courage may undoubtedly be, they can be misdirected; and only when used as a complement to generosity, and with respect for fellow men and women, may they preserve for each individual the confident security each craves in relationships with family, group or nation.

The lines of descent of the main protagonists in the tribe of Abs whose stories are told in the book

The lord ZUHAIR ibn Jazima
m. TEMADHUR bint Amr ibn Shedid

Their ten sons included: SHAS, QAIS, MALIK the Prince, HARITH

Their daughter was: MUTAJERIDA

*

A close family connection of Zuhair's:

ZAIYAD ibn Abdallah
m. FATIMA bint Husaib

Their ten sons included: RABIA, AMARA

*

The sons of KARAD, a member of the tribe, included:

First, SHEDDAD
who m. SAMIYA

But who was, by ZEBEEBA the Black Slave, father of 'ANTAR

And secondly, MALEC
who m. SHERIYA

And whose son was AMR, and whose daughter
was 'ABLA, 'Antar's love and later his wife

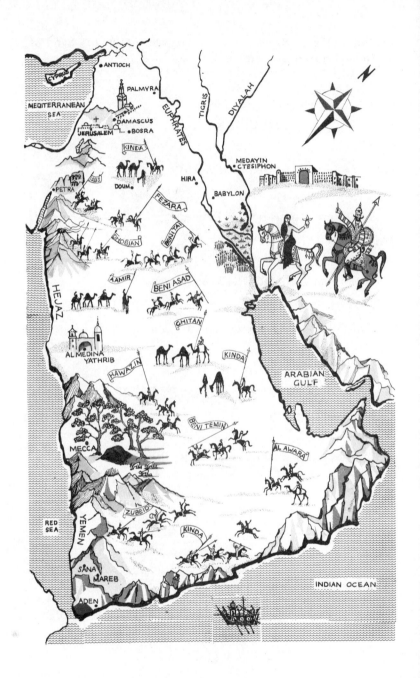

The First Story

THE TRIBES AND
THEIR LEADERS

The names of their ancestors are known names: Noah and Shem, Cush and Cana'an, and the giant Nimrod, the mighty hunter and the cursed of God since in his reign men turned from worshipping the One and worshipped idols. Their ancestors sprang from Abraham, the Friend of God, and Isma'il, his eldest son, who did not shrink from sacrificing himself to God's will, though he was mercifully spared. The Friend of God and his beloved Hajar rested once with the boy Isma'il in the place we now call Mecca, where Abraham's footprint can be seen to this day; and there Abraham raised the Ka'aba, the House of God, and there the spring Zamzam flowed for the quenching of Isma'il's thirst. And after these came Adnan and Qahtan; and from among them Maad; Medher and Nizar, and many more brave men and lovely women, and the tribes formed and re-formed and spread over the desert land, learning its secrets, loving its beauty, battling with its harsh conditions. And God loved the men and women of His desert lands and He gave them, instead of diadems, turbans; instead of walled houses, tents; instead of ramparts, bare swords; and instead of laws He gave them poetry.

And among the valiant leaders of these people who drove their flocks over the desert in search of pasture was Mohelhil, who died young and whose cousins divided his rights and property among themselves, settling with the tribes of Abs and Adnan, the riders of the desert, the riders of death.

And Jazima, overlord of Mohelhil ibn Rabia, had exacted

19

tribute from many tribes, but the leader of the Riyan, who was a woman, refused him this tribute, and when the two armies met to resolve this defiance it was agreed that the dispute should be settled by mortal combat between the two leaders, the brave Jazima and the defiant Robab on her jet-black horse. Now Robab's horsemanship was so skilful that Jazima's superior strength was unavailing, and she struck him down in the sight of all his tribe, and calamity and despair came upon the Abs people. They compared Robab with the Arab princess Zenobia, who led her father's men into battle and defeated even the Romans in the old days when Palmyra was still a proud city at the height of its beauty.

Now among Jazima's ten noble sons, three are remembered to this day: Amr, who was drowned in the pools of Dhat al Arsad, and who, men say, yet reappeared in the form of a gazelle; Asyed, a learned man who could both read and write; and Zuhair, whom our story will present as the worthy leader of a brave tribe, and one to whom the virtues of loyalty and hospitality were paramount.

Zuhair avenged his father's death, killing Robab and dispersing her people, the Riyan — and from that tribe he won for his own many flocks and camels, women and children and servants; and in the manner of the Arabs he treated them with courtesy and kindness. And Zuhair led a tribe in which the virtues of the sons and daughters of the desert were apparent. The sons were brave and skilful in arms, yet generous to both friends and enemies, rating all men equal before God. Quick and eloquent they were in the use of their language, their greatest gift, in which poetical prowess brought fame recognized by friend and foe alike at the great assemblies of Ukaz. The daughters, too, were schooled by the rough severity of the desert to value humour and independence. They were less subordinate to their menfolk than women of the cities, they were beautiful, and swift in repartee, modest yet not ignorant of life's realities; and they shared with their men an immense ardour for passionate love, and an unquenchable reverence for honour.

So it happened that the good Zuhair established his hold over the tribes by strength and virtue, and after he had celebrated his growing successes by journeying to the sanctuary of Mecca (where no blood could ever be shed and where even criminals could find shelter, and where men, purified by abstention from all physical indulgence, might ponder on the divinities as yet not totally revealed to the desert people) he returned to his own tents, and began his search for a wife of noble enough lineage to share his high position.

This then is the story of Zuhair's courtship and of the marriage which brought him so near disaster and yet which established the tribe of Abs firmly in its rightful ascendancy.

Zuhair's messengers told him of the beautiful Temadhur, fairest of the daughters of Amr ibn Shedid. And the lord Zuhair found himself sick with love for Temadhur though he had not seen her, and sick at heart because her father allowed no man to address her; and he longed for Temadhur as a thirsty man longs for water. Thus it was in desperation that he conceived a plan. He sent his messengers to Amr, and by flattery and courtesy persuaded him to visit Abs territory and to pitch his tents not far from the Abs people. Every evening at sundown Amr was an honoured guest of Zuhair.

Now the small tribe of Ghorab was subservient to the lord Zuhair, and he plotted with their leader, and one morning at daybreak the Ghorab surrounded the tents of Amr and attacked them; and during the skirmish Zuhair rode up with his men and drove off the Ghorab, who were afterwards rewarded for their loyalty. Then he saw Temadhur standing at the entrance to her tent, watching in dismay while the flocks of her family were driven off, despite the gallant efforts of her father and her brothers, who fought like lions. And Temadhur was like a slim reed growing by the water's edge: her skin glowed in the dawning sun, her cheeks were red as anemones and her hair, dishevelled by the dawn wind, was as black as the centres of these desert flowers.

The lord Zuhair's men beat off the Ghorab and rescued Temadhur, and in the evening Zuhair ordered a banquet at which Amr, father of Temadhur, was given a place of honour and much wine to drink. And the old man's heart melted in gratitude and he cried, 'O mighty and magnanimous lord, I am your grateful servant. My tongue cannot describe your virtues. God has given me no gift more cherished than my daughter, Temadhur, from whom I have kept all suitors. Yet now, O lord, before all this noble assembly, I beg of you to accept her as your hand-maiden.'

And all those assembled there begged Zuhair to agree, and this he willingly did, ordering many rich presents to be given to

Amr, and suggesting that Temadhur be honoured by marriage to him. So she was brought in with her maidens under the hastily erected marriage canopy. And Zuhair's ruse thus succeeded, and he and Temadhur, who appeared sweeter than sleep to the wearied eye, were united to their mutual joy, and the feasting lasted seven days.

Now it happened that Zuhair's happiness in his success rendered him both arrogant and over-confident, and he told Temadhur of the stratagem by which he had obtained her for his own; and Temadhur, for all her love, became angry. She resented, above all, the way in which her family had been deprived of a brideprice. Yet she retained her shrewdness and good sense, so that when next her lord invited her caresses, she turned from him, saying, 'Shame on you, who pretend to the Arab virtue of generosity and yet seize the daughter of a gallant man by force and deprive him of the brideprice!'

And Zuhair was greatly irritated by this rebuke, and he answered sharply, 'Indeed, I have in no way been mean or avaricious; had your father allowed me to court you in the normal manner of the tribes you would have marvelled at the gifts I would have offered for your hand.'

But Temadhur was determined to show up his deceit and his meanness, and she went on: 'You have boasted that you won me by violence and cunning — you shall see that we are more cunning than you.' Then was Zuhair angry, but Temadhur pressed home her advantage, reminding him that he who speaks too freely may earn a bitter reply, and that he who treats a woman contemptuously will encounter difficulties. 'Know you,' she added, 'that I am but the sister of the girl you beheld at the entrance to her tent. You have been deceived, even as you deceived my father with your false hospitality. I am Khida‘a, and my beauty is as nothing compared to the loveliness of the real Temadhur, who is renowned among all the daughters of Arabia. Now it is too late, and had you not boasted to me I would never have told you of this.'

The lord Zuhair was appalled at his predicament, and begged his wife to tell him how he could find proof of her story. So she told him that only disguised as a woman, or as a merchant or a perfumer, could he enter her mother's tents and see for himself the beautiful Temadhur. And Zuhair mused sadly that only he could discover the truth. So he instructed his men that on the morrow he would be absent,

and through a trusted servant he obtained the perfumes and
medicines of a perfumer, and a perfumer's clothing, and he
lay down to sleep alone. But Temadhur also disguised herself,
and she dressed as a boy so as to ride more swiftly and safely
to her father's tents; and she rose earlier than her husband
and surprised her family before the stars had set, and she
kissed her mother and she greeted her father and her brothers
and bade them await the lord's arrival hidden in the tent.
She said to them, 'We women will detain him and then you
must fall upon him and bind him fast, and we shall not release
him until a good brideprice be arranged, else shall we be a
scandal among the tribes. And if he abuses you, you will
answer that though he is a lord, justice demands that our
behaviour to him be as good or as bad as his behaviour to us.'
So the brothers hid themselves, and Temadhur dressed once
more as a girl in her sister's bright silks, and she was as lovely as
a cluster of anemones blooming under the desert rocks after
rain, and she blackened her eyelashes with kohl, and she wore
no veil.

As the dawn broke Zuhair appeared, his eyes darting
anxiously from face to face among the women, like those of a
desert fox seeking out its prey. He spoke to the mother of
Temadhur and entered the tent where Temadhur awaited
him, and was much confused to see her there, unveiled upon
the cushions and in all her beauty. Zuhair asked the old lady
what was the name of the damsel, and she answered,
'Temadhur, for when the lord Zuhair was offered Temadhur
in marriage, we deceived him, giving him our daughter
Khida'a instead; yet this he knows not, and for ourselves we
mean to marry our daughter to a more noble chief.' Now
Zuhair felt he would die of rage, and he planned within
himself to carry off this lovely maiden, but her brothers leaped
upon him like leopards from the rocks, and they bound him
hand and foot before he could make a move.

Then arose Temadhur from her couch and she cried, 'Now,
O lord, what think you of your situation and your artifice?'
And Zuhair was in despair, but the knowledge that he was
indeed married to Temadhur after all gave him strength, and
the sight of her beauty revived him and he asked her what her
terms were for his release. And Temadhur demanded protection for her family and a confirmation of the marriage by the
transfer of flocks and herds, and an acknowledgement of his

misdeeds, and all to be sworn before God and by the Friend of God, Abraham, and by the holy well of Zamzam which sprang up in the desert place to refresh Isma'il.

When Zuhair heard all this, he smiled up at Temadhur and acknowledged his misdeeds, and felt his admiration for her glow within him, and he said, 'I will give you five hundred camels and you must let me go.' But Temadhur answered, 'Nay, that would pay only for one hour as your wife.' 'Another five hundred, then,' he offered, but she replied, 'Even for a single day this would be insufficient.' So Zuhair laughed and said to Temadhur, 'O Temadhur, if you must reckon up every hour of each night and of each day, and value them as you would value merchandise in a market, you would take from me all my possessions and my flocks and my herds both of he-camels and she-camels, and I would be bereft.' And upon that she too smiled and ordered her brothers to unloose him, and she ordered her maid-servant to bring coffee; and over the coffee they bargained as a husband and wife should, till they had settled the business between them, and the gift was arranged thus: one thousand he-camels and she-camels, and twenty horses, and fifty men-servants, and fifty maid-servants, and all this Zuhair promised, swearing upon the holy shrines of Mecca and the sanctuary where all are safe, and upon the spring Zamzam where Isma'il and Hajar drank. Then they feasted with Temadhur's family till night came, and in the darkness Temadhur and Zuhair returned to their own tent, very happy in one another's company and with new respect for each other. Their love increased, and Zuhair gave Temadhur, too, many valuable presents; and no one knew what had passed that day. And as the years went by Temadhur gave birth to ten sons, all valorous as lions, and honourable; and to one daughter, Mutajerida, and Temadhur was known among the tribes as one who had borne ten sons.

The lord Zuhair ruled the tribes with skill and honesty. And into this fellowship comes the great 'Antar, whose love for Zuhair he celebrated in royal verse:

O my lord, my generous Zuhair,
Wherever thou goest, death goes before thee
To destroy all enemies.

Help, then, the solitary one who weeps the night through,
    My support, my stay against foes
    Who are jealous of my exaltation.

Here is the lord to whom princes must bow and do homage,
Here is a refuge for all who come in grief,
Here is one who has assuaged my grief.

May fortune never deprive me of this lord.
May he live eternally in his joy and happiness.

The Second Story

'ANTAR'S YOUTH

In the tribe of Abs were included Zuhair's ten sons, of whom Shas, Qais and Malik the Prince were remembered; and Zuhair held dominion also over other tribes, among them the tribes led by Karad and Zaiyad.

Karad's sons were Sheddad and Malec; and Zaiyad's sons were Rabia and Amara. All these men were warriors and good servants of the tribe, but the Prince was especially revered as a man of peace, one who used his wisdom and his courage to settle quarrels by means other than violence. It is, however, with Sheddad ibn Karad that we are concerned in this story.

There came a day when Sheddad, mounted upon his famous mare Jirwet, was riding with nine other warriors in the country surrounding Sherebeh. And it happened that as they rode over the foothills of Mount Aja and Mount Selma, into the country of Qahtan, they came unseen upon a brave sight in the valley below them. The encampment of the Jezeela tribe lay there: a rich encampment, with its black tents, its silken banners streaming in the wind, and the shadows streaming out over the sand before the rising sun. Men and maidens moved between the tents, and servants from foreign lands, often with golden or ruddy hair, were busy at their work. The encampment was far too vast for an attack by ten men, even such men as Sheddad and his comrades, and Sheddad retired, and they circled the camp like kites wheeling, watching from the skies for every movement of small creatures on the sand below. Thus it was that they came upon grazing grounds where a thousand camels ranged over the thin green grass and the blue iris flowers, guarded only by a beautiful Negress and two small boys as dark-skinned as their mother.

In this moment the whole future of Sheddad and of his tribe was changed. Sheddad's heart glowed at the sight of the lovely slave. She was young, and she walked with all the spring and grace of Africa. Her skin was smooth as ebony, her wrists and ankles delicately formed as the bones of a gazelle. Her teeth, when she smiled, sparkled like hailstones in the sunshine after a desert storm, and her eyes burned brown like polished cornelian.

Thrilled by her beauty, as his companions were delighted by the abundance of well-fed camels, Sheddad and the nine captured the flock with its guardian and her two small helpers, and drove all away across the slopes towards home. But the cloud of dust they raised warned a party of Qahtan, who swarmed out from their camp to do battle for their flocks. Great indeed was the battle which followed. But it came about that Sheddad was enabled to hold off the Qahtan, and he and his warriors escaped over the desert with many camels, and with the Negress and the boys unharmed. The name of the Negress was Zebeeba, and her boys were Shiboob — so famous a name — and Jarir.

Sheddad and Zebeeba together tasted the delights of love on the shores of the pools of Dhat al Arsad as they journeyed homewards, and the nine men disputed as to who should take the camels and who should finally enjoy the favours of the captive Zebeeba; and so it was that the dispute came to the notice of the lord Zuhair and of his Qadi, Sidi el Fezari, for in his presence Sheddad declared that he would renounce all other prizes if he could be awarded the Negress and her children. So the bargain was struck before Zuhair, and so great was Sheddad's passion for Zebeeba that he installed her, though but a slave, in a good tent decorated with silks, and here she loved him. Then in the course of time she bore him a son, 'Antar, and from the first Zuhair took an interest in this child.

Now Sheddad was a poet, and he sang of his love:

All my strength, all my valour, O Love, do I not draw
from thee? Is it not solely

By the dark ribbon of thy tresses, O gentle dove, is it
   not by the silken skein of thy frailty,
That the surge of valour mounts within me, all my strength,
   all my courage?

The beauty of these dark Africans, if you but understand it,
     Surpasses the loveliness of the fair,
     Or of the nut-brown maidens of India.

Who can describe the supple swing of her walk,
     The fascination of her dark eyes,
Which would enchant the angels themselves?

If it were not black, what value would there be in a beauty-
   spot contrasted with an ivory cheek?
If it were not black, would musk remain musk?

     And without the dark of the night how couldst thou gaze
     Upon the dawn?

So large, so strong, was the baby 'Antar even from the
moment of his birth, that he was the envy of every man and
woman in the tribe, with his dark complexion, wide eyes, thick
lips — his powerful shoulders and his grasping hands. Stories
of his feats of strength were soon passing from mouth to
mouth. If he was refused milk he would growl like a lion; by
the time he was weaned he could ward off any roaming dog, or
mischievous children months older than himself. Sheddad
recognized in him his own great power, and he rejoiced.

Before a very few years had passed, 'Antar was able to drive
the flocks and herds out to graze, with his two brothers,
Shiboob and Jarir; and in the desert pastures his savage temperament was mellowed. He learned patience from the desert's
peace, perseverance from its harshness, self-control from
caring for the flocks. Born into a family of slaves, his proud
nature rejected from the first any slur on his birth, and he
swore to become an equal in the tribe.

During his boyhood he set about self-training, caring for the
ewes and she-camels, seeking to understand the ways of the
horse, the mare and the foal. Here on the desert plains he
learned to ride with all the skills of the tribesman whose horse,
like a sailing boat, can give him freedom to roam the desert
and to amass its spoils, as a fisherman can master and harvest
the sea. 'Antar sought out the gnarled trees in the foothills and

practised throwing his spear at their trunks until finally he was better accomplished, and more feared, than any other among the servant-boys. Among the children of the tribe, both slave and free, he made his friends; and he learned from them to play with, and to value, the desert's herbs and flowers, its insects and birds and wildlife. In these formative days, 'Antar observed his elders and the leaders of the tribes, admiring courage and generosity where he found it, deprecating cruelty and meanness where it was displayed; and at the tribal assemblies, he listened entranced to the poetry recited there.

Now it happened that on a certain day in winter time, when food was scarce and the desert wind swept up the wolf-grey clouds from the far-off ocean, and when rain-storms chased thundering across the land, 'Antar's flocks were threatened by a wolf of enormous size — a wolf whose eyes flashed lightning as the heavens did, whose growl was like the thunder, and whose hairs stiffened around his neck like twigs of the tamarisk frozen in the winter wind. But 'Antar, unafraid, flung himself upon this creature of the storm and killed it with one blow of his shepherd's crook. Then, cutting off its head and four paws and scraping its pelt to use against the cold, he returned to the camp singing:

'O wolf, desert wolf, you hurled yourself at death,
    You have become my prey.

Are not these pastures meant for my flocks,
    And my herds?

Your blood now flows upon the soil.
    You tried to scatter my herds.
    Did you not realize that I am terrible as a lion?
See how I have dealt with you, you desert cur!'

All the dogs of the camp welcomed him with their barking, smelling the dead wolf, and Zebeeba hurried to tell Sheddad of his son's achievement.

As 'Antar grew in power and virtue he became aware of his great strength and desired to use this gift in the service of those less strong than himself. And while he was yet a boy, he brought his flocks to the wells one evening, and around the wells were the flocks of many in the tribe, including those few animals belonging to the poor and feeble, some of them women alone. Now it happened that Shas, second son of the lord Zuhair, owned a slave whose name was Daji, and this Daji took delight in bullying and tormenting those weaker than himself. On this day, as 'Antar was driving his flocks to the water, Daji was teasing and tormenting an old woman who had lost her husband and children, and had no protector in the tribe; and Daji, in his wickedness, knocked the old woman down in the mud, in front of everyone, and she lay there with her poor garments in disarray, ashamed and mocked by all the crowd. Now to 'Antar the honour of all women was a very precious thing, and having helped her to her feet from the slippery mud beside the wells, he challenged Daji — a grown man — to cease his cruelty, crying, 'Shame upon you, son of an adulterer, since when is it permitted to dishonour an Arab woman! May God's punishment descend upon you and all who act as you have acted!'

In his arrogance Daji almost fainted in indignation, and he struck 'Antar a terrible blow, but 'Antar rallied and, although only a boy, seized Daji and lifted him in both hands, and hurled him to the ground with such force that his spirit left his body. Now was the crowd both fearful and angry, and 'Antar would have been the object of their attack, but as the fight was beginning the third son of Zuhair rode by.

This son was known always as the Prince, for he was a mild and gentle man beloved by all the tribe for the sweetness of his disposition and the serenity of his behaviour. He had been disgusted by Daji's bullying, seen from afar off, and his eyes had filled with tears at the old woman's shame. He took 'Antar's part in the struggle and with a few sharp words restrained the crowd, showing his contempt for their cowardice in attacking a mere boy.

Then were Shas and the Prince divided over the death of Daji and 'Antar's intervention. But Shas was pacified by a gift of ten slaves, and the Prince took 'Antar under his protection, and he said to his father, Zuhair, 'One day, O my father, you will see that this Negro slave will be a model among men, a defender of women and children. He will eschew violence and follow the path of justice.' Finally the Prince returned 'Antar to Sheddad's care. And Sheddad was much alarmed at the audacity of 'Antar's deeds, but Zuhair and the Prince admired his valour, and all the tribe remembered his courage.

The Third Story

THE CHILDREN OF THE TRIBE

Every morning before the sun was too hot the children of the tribe would swarm out over the pasture and the desert, slave children and free children together, the older ones practising their various skills and playing together, the younger ones tumbling and romping with the young animals as though they were a part of the same flock. All of them learned much from these days of freedom, and by the time they were seven years old and were pressed into useful service by their elders, both boys and girls were accomplished in many ways.

The boys could ride as though they had become an integral part of their horses. They could track domestic animals and wild animals, and knew how to avoid attack from wolf or jackal, and where the dreaded hyena might be lurking. They could distinguish the markings and the trails in the sand of all the desert snakes; they matched scorpions together in combat and laughed at the antics of the praying mantis. They could throw a stone, and fly a hawk, and were beginning to be skilled at hunting with javelin, or with bow and arrow.

The girls, too, could ride well, and they had learnt the names and habits of the many plants growing under the rocky hilltops and outcrops after rain, on the stone-covered slopes or on the sand itself. They knew their medicinal value and how to prepare ointments and draughts and dyes from these bitter and sweet-smelling shrubs and flowers. With the boys they would stalk and sometimes capture birds for the pot. They were familiar with the swift little quail, the black partridge,

31

the sharp-winged and golden sand-grouse, and the great barred and whiskered bustard. They could recognize the flocks of migrants which traversed the periphery of the desert, and, lying on the soft, warm sand, could wonder at the kites and eagles moving so slowly in the sky above, or the pied storks trailing their long pink legs as they flocked north for the nesting.

Girls and boys knew where to seek those edible thistle-roots much beloved by all, and the great desert truffles growing beneath the sand and only hinting at their presence by a random crevice in the surface. When the boys fought their scorpions, the girls, perhaps tired of warfare, would collect in a corner of cloth the burnished beetles or beautiful desert spiders, big as a thumb's nail and covered like Suleiman himself in scarlet velvet. In hard times they would bring in for the tribe to eat the hard fruits of the lote tree — that thorny, stunted bush which had once borne sweet fruit in paradise, and which now yielded such a meagre harvest, and whose cruel thorns, it was said, were once crushed down upon the brow of the prophet Issa before he died.

So the children played, free as the lambs and kids and foals of the tribes' flocks, learning the skills without which they could not survive on the shores of this sandy ocean where one infringement of the rules of God would assuredly lead to death. As they grew older they would, one by one, settle to work, though the more adventurous might enjoy a further year or two of expeditions until finally it became imperative for the boys and girls to separate; and the girls would perhaps reluctantly settle down to a more secluded existence, learning how to spin and weave the tent cloth, and the patterned rugs which were the pride and trademark of the tribe. Yet still in the long hot hours, or in the short winter rains, they would gather around some favourite to hear stories of other tribes and other times, and here are two of them:

Once there was, or there was not, a horse called Dahis, the Thruster, and this is a story which especially delighted 'Abla who, as a young girl, had had so great a love for the wide desert spaces and for horses which could be mastered and trained to skim the soft sand and the stony slopes like flying birds. And this is 'Abla who was to become 'Antar's beloved. Now the father of this horse was once seen by a slave who had been sent into the desert searching for a flock of she-asses which his master had lost, as once were lost the she-asses of Kish, son of Abiel — he who was the father of Saul, the first king of the Jews. The slave returned to his master and said, 'O my master, although I have not found the she-asses which I sought on your behalf, yet did I see a horse of remarkable power and beauty, and I heard the story of this horse, and the story is no less remarkable than the horse itself. For the story goes,' said the slave, anxious to appease his master, 'that this was Ocab, a horse of intelligence, and owned by one Karim, son of Wahab, who valued it greatly. And it was the custom of Karim's daughter, Nafisa, to ride Ocab in the desert with her young companions, boys and girls together, for as yet none was more than ten years old. And Nafisa, mounted upon Ocab, rode further and faster than the rest, racing with them and glorying in the swiftness and spirit of her steed, until at length she came to a pool. Now by the pool there was a mare grazing on the sweet green grass, and the mare was irresistibly beautiful to Ocab, for she was on heat. And as Nafisa and Ocab rode nearer, the mare, whose name was Helwa, lifted her golden head and whinnied softly to Ocab, and thereafter Nafisa could not restrain him. So Nafisa in her modesty slipped down from the bare back of Ocab, for she rode him with no saddle, and hid her face among the bushes; and Ocab fulfilled his desire for Helwa, and they mated there by the waterside. And Ocab's halter broke as he strained towards Helwa, so Nafisa had to ride home with a knotted halter, and it was dark before she returned. And Nafisa's mother was both fearful and angry and said, "It is evident, Nafisa, that you are too old and too daring to accompany the children on these desert rides, henceforth you must stay with me, and with your aunts and cousins, for it is not prudent to venture so far into the desert alone." And Nafisa wept for her lost freedom for she was still a child.

'On the following day,' said the slave, 'a servant came to Karim her father saying, "I have mended the broken halter with which Ocab and your daughter returned from the desert," and Karim inquired of Nafisa why the halter had broken, and Nafisa in her modesty would say nothing; but later she confessed to her mother what had happened by the pool. When he heard of it Karim was greatly disturbed for he recognized Nafisa's description of the golden mare Helwa, the apple of his cousin's eye; and his cousin was Jabri, son of Awad, the owner of the mare.

'Nafisa mounted on Ocab rode further and faster than the rest'

'Then did Karim tell his cousin what had occurred,' said the slave, 'and Jabri was furious, for he had not intended that his mare should foal, and he cursed Karim, and he cursed his slaves who had allowed Helwa to stray from the camp, and he sought out Helwa, hoping to repair any damage which had been done. The slaves in great fear held and fettered Helwa with their hands, and indeed with ropes, and Jabri sent for the biggest cooking-pot available, and in it he made a mixture of white clay from the oasis and water. He bared his arm to the elbow and grasped a dripping handful of white clay, and he thrust his arm within Helwa the mare, with a view,' said the slave, 'to destroying what was originally ordained by God to exist.'

Now at this point the slave broke off his narrative, begging pardon of his master for not having recovered the she-asses which had been lost; and his master forgave him, for he was curious to know what transpired. And the story continued thus: God ordained that the seed planted by Ocab should grow, and in due time the mare foaled, and her foal was a perfect foal, and was named Dahis, that is 'The Thruster', in remembrance of Jabri's operation. And passions cooled between the two cousins, Karim and Jabri.

Yet later did Karim steal both Helwa and the foal from his cousin, and a war ensued between the two factions of the tribe, and some say that the war lasted for forty years, and it was known as the War of the Horse. But some say that it lasted only a short time, and that Karim in his nobility surrendered the mare and her foal to Jabri who was himself thus shamed into returning them with many additional horses and camels into the bargain. But war or no war, Dahis is remembered for the part he played in the great race with the mare Ghabra, owned by Hadifa, between whose tribe, the A'amin, and the Riyan lay enmity.

This then is the story of the great race. It was decided that the quarrel between the Riyan and the A'amin should not be resolved by tribal fighting, or by mortal combat between the two leaders, but by the matching of the two horses in a race; for so long-standing was the enmity between the two tribes that even the old men and the story-tellers had forgotten the prime cause of the quarrel. So the leaders of the tribes met at a feast to decide upon the affair, and much wine was drunk and all became confused, wagering with each other as to the result of

35

the race and arguing with passion as to the length of the route and the powers of the two horses.

Finally it was agreed that the length of the race should be forty arrow shots from the bow of Ayas, son of Mansur, a Fazari horseman and a proverbial archer. And the route to be followed was decided also. And the training of the two horses was to be forty days in length.

Now there were many within the two tribes of Riyan and A'amin who had individual quarrels of their own and were determined to use the occasion of the race to resolve these to their own advantage, and to avenge the honour of their leaders and their tribes; for these men did not care to see such matters settled peaceably, and they plotted with much cunning to interfere with the race.

So it was that on the fortieth day Dahis and Ghabra were brought to the oasis, gleaming like silk, the one golden like his dam, the other yellow as broom with a black mane and a black tail; and both were in fine shape for the race. But the rider of Dahis objected to the length of the arrow shots and claimed, moreover, that there had only been thirty-nine of these instead of forty, and that he would not race. Now he did this to dismay Ghabra and her rider, thinking, They will run less well tomorrow. And the race was postponed. And on the second day, the rider of Ghabra objected to the explanation of the course to be followed, saying that it had not been made clear to him which hillocks were to be encircled and that he would not race. Now he did this to dismay Dahis, thinking, They will run less well tomorrow. And the race was postponed.

But on the third day the onlookers were impatient and would permit no more delay, and the two horses were led to the starting-place, and as the starter's sword flashed downwards in the pale light, they leaped forwards like two of Ayas's arrows shot from his bow, and it was dawn. First Dahis was ahead, then Ghabra, and thrice they changed position before they swept out of sight behind the slope of a hill, and as they reached the slope of the hill there was a flash of metal in the sunlight, for an A'amini slave sprang out upon Dahis, hurling at him a stone, but the slave was killed by his enemy hidden near by, a Riyani who felled him with a spear. And as the horses reappeared from behind the slope of the hill, there was another flash of metal in the sunlight, for a Riyan slave sprang out upon Ghabra, hurling at her a stone, but the slave was killed by his enemy hidden near by, an A'amini who felled him with a spear. And though both the horse and the mare were bruised and frightened, yet did their riders urge them on at such speed that they disappeared from view on the far side of the lake, and they raced far further than the forty bowshots, and the sun was high in the sky when the two were seen again.

Again they ran into misfortune, for a slave of the Riyan and a slave of the A'amin had been posted at the end of a narrow ravine, one on each side of the outlet, and each was hidden behind the rocks and the oleander bushes, and hidden also the one from the other. The ravine was full of soft sand, and the Riyani slave had asked his master, who plotted against Ghabra, 'Sir, if I am to try to injure this mare, how can I take good aim in the dust since she is coloured like the dust itself?' And the A'amini slave had asked his master the same question about Dahis, adding only that Dahis was golden like his dam and would be concealed in the yellow dust. Whereupon the two masters had independently devised a scheme whereby, on see-ing his horse enter the ravine on a stony track, and before the dust arose, each slave would lift up a bag of pebbles and would drop these one by one. Both masters and both slaves worked out the distance, and in each case the number of pebbles agreed upon was nine, so that as the mare and the horse galloped through the ravine in clouds of dust, the slaves let their pebbles fall, to the ninth one — and the tenth pebble each slave hurled into the billowing dust. And it happened that the horse and the mare passed without injury, but each slave was struck by the other's pebble and lay stunned in the soft sand; but the horse and the mare swept on, and at noonday they appeared once more at full gallop, approaching the side of the oasis from which they had started. And some say that they arrived together at the spot where the two lances marked the winning post, with not so much as a spider's thread between them; and they say that both Dahis and Ghabra had tears streaming down their faces from the pain of the stones with which they had been attacked; but others say that they were joined in the race by an 'afrit who raced with them in the form of a man, and outpaced them both; and some again say that this man was no other than Shiboob, brother of 'Antar, who knew so well the paths and ways of the desert. But it is known that the close running of the horse and the mare brought the quarrels of the two tribes to an end for a time at least, and the horses were bathed at the oasis, and their wounds dressed, and the two tribes celebrated the great race with three days of feasting and dancing, and with hawking contests and music and poetry.

As for the story about the 'afrit, since it was repeated by 'Abla in her own day, and before Shiboob was grown a man, then may it not well be true? And indeed this story was a favourite story with 'Abla when she was a child, since she so loved to ride. And when she became a woman she would tell it to the children of the tribe, and all would laugh, especially at the predicament of Nafisa who could not control Ocab and Helwa at the waterside. But Amr, brother to 'Abla, would not laugh because he thought the tale was a coarse tale, not fit for his sister's recounting, nor did he like her admiration for Nafisa, who rode so well, for Amr was jealous of his sister's horsemanship.

The Fourth Story
'ABLA

It was the custom in those far-off days that the Arab women should drink sheep's milk as they arose in the early morning, and this milk would be brought to the tents of the leaders of the tribe by a servant who had seen to it that the warm milk had been cooled in the dawn breeze. 'Antar performed this service for Samiya, wife of his father Sheddad, and for Sheriya, the wife of Malec, son of Karad, uncle of 'Antar. Malec was a man of suspicious nature, and one in whom envy and jealousy strove with arrogance for mastery of his soul. He lacked the graces of magnanimity so precious to the Arab people. His son, Amr, inherited his father's meanness, but his daughter, 'Abla, displayed in her person and in her personality all the gifts most admired in a daughter of the desert. Her merry humour, her kindness to the unfortunate and her respect for her elders rendered her a byword in the tribe; and as she emerged from childhood to womanhood her beauty was fast becoming legendary.

Yet, for all her good humour, there was little love between sister and brother, 'Abla and Amr. Indeed, he disliked what he considered to be her lack of dignity. For Amr was proud of the nobility of his family which he shared by birth, and he had not realized, as had his sister, that noble behaviour should accompany a high position. Moreover, as children, 'Abla had far excelled him as a rider of horses, for in those days she had sought to emulate Robab, and the Princess Zenobia, who led her father's men into battle in the days when Palmyra was still a fair city at the height of its beauty; and 'Abla would still recount the story of the conception of the mare, Dahis, the Thruster, and of the Great Race, but Amr did not like these stories.

And it happened at this time — and it was spring-time — that when 'Antar entered the women's tent to serve the cool milk, he surprised his cousin 'Abla at her toilet, for she sat unveiled and only half-dressed while her mother combed and plaited her long black hair. 'Abla cried out in her embarrassment and fled across the tent, her hair flowing behind her as a silken pennant floats in the wind; and 'Antar, though almost bereft of his senses by her beauty, yet retained enough of them to observe the loveliness of her form — her ivory skin, and her firm breasts rising cleanly as do the desert dunes in the moonlight; and the rustle of her dress was soft as the wings of starlings flocking to the wadi in the evening hours. So 'Antar lost his heart to his cousin 'Abla, who was yet so far above him in rank that never could he aspire to marriage with her, being but a slave although of noble blood.

On the following morning, as he entered the tent again, he was overcome with embarrassment, for 'Abla cried in her merry way, 'It seems, friend, that I must rise earlier than you to preserve my modesty! See how well I have done today, almost beating the dawn itself!' And she laughed, and her aunt and her mother laughed too; but as for poor 'Antar, his love and his confusion were so great that he offered the sheep's milk to his fair cousin before he had served it to the elder women. Then Samiya, wife of Sheddad, was furious, and drove him from the tent. But 'Abla smiled to herself and was not unaware of 'Antar's strength and comeliness for all that his colour was black as the pitch which oozes over the sand at the foot of the Persian mountains in the far desert.

In those days, as in our own, there were plots and intrigues among the slaves and servants, and among their masters too. Samiya's anger with 'Antar was exploited now by Zajir, slave of Rabia, who bore a grudge against 'Antar. Zajir told Samiya how 'Antar had learned his camel-riding and his horse-riding at the expense of the herds, and how he had injured the few and precious trees of the desert fringes by aiming at them his javelins and spears. And Samiya sought her husband and complained to him of the black slave who could not care for the animals in his charge nor appreciate the true position of an elder woman's rank compared to that of young 'Abla.

And Sheddad was angry, and seizing his son he beat him cruelly. But 'Antar, although he was already as strong as his father, suffered the beating in all humility because he respected his father and his father's position in the tribe. Zebeeba came also to her son and warned him to remember his lowly position. But 'Antar, who lay bound after the beating, burst his bonds simply by flexing his muscles, and seizing a horse he followed the slave Zajir into the desert, and there killed him for his treachery. 'For,' he said to himself, 'a man should, if he have a grievance, speak openly to his opponent of the quarrel, nor should he secretly persuade a woman to speak for him.'

Among the leaders of the tribe, too, there were feuds and dissension, for Rabia, clever and ambitious as he was, disliked the Prince and his brothers, and Sheddad and Malec swayed to one side or the other side, but all respected and feared, or loved, lord Zuhair.

Now when 'Antar had killed the second slave he sought protection from the Prince against Rabia's wrath, and the Prince made up his mind to settle the affair with no further bloodshed, for the Prince was a kindly man. He sought the elders in their assembly, and all rose as he entered, giving and receiving the greetings. And the Prince, still standing, turned to Rabia and said, 'Cousin, I greet you, and if you love me I would ask a favour of you.' 'Indeed I love you,' growled Rabia, who did no such thing, but to whom the courtesies were important as they are to all true Arabs. 'Give me then, I pray, your slave Zajir,' continued the Prince. Now Rabia valued Zajir, and thought he was still alive, and to give himself time to think he reproached the Prince, saying, 'Sit down in your place, I beg of you, my cousin, for are we not all standing because you continue so?' 'Do you wish I should sit down, and do you love me?' queried the Prince. 'Then favour me with your slave, else I remain standing and may disbelieve your love.' Rabia had no choice but to agree, and the company was seated, and when Zuhair joined them, then did the Prince reveal Zajir's death, and he explained to Rabia that this unfortunate fact was now of little consequence to the dishonest slave's former master. And Zuhair and his elders smiled at the Prince's trick, and Rabia appeared pacified by the gift of two new slaves.

But afterwards, Rabia sought out his brother, Amara the Coxcomb, who hated the Prince, and together they approached

Sheddad, and they persuaded Sheddad that his Negro son was becoming a menace to the unity of the tribe, and Sheddad agreed, and a plot was laid to kill 'Antar when he was alone and unprotected in the desert. 'For,' said these uncles of his, and his father, 'Lord Zuhair and the Prince think well of 'Antar, but may we not be overwhelmed by a veritable ocean of calamities and misfortunes if he continues to live among us? He must die.'

Now 'Antar's flocks were grazing in a secluded valley far from the camp, and 'Antar was composing to himself a poem in praise of his beautiful cousin 'Abla, when an enormous lion burst through the bushes and confronted him. And behind the rocks, on the other side of the valley, 'Antar's father and his two uncles crept up in hiding, planning to murder him. But 'Antar thrust the crook he carried between the lion's teeth and, advancing, seized the animal's upper jaw in one hand and its lower jaw in the other hand, and tore the lion in two. Then he skinned the lion and burned its flesh, and started scraping its pelt for his own use; and as he scraped he sang:

'O lion, father of lion cubs and king of the sandy wastes
    and of the animals which dwell there,
How strong thou art, how proud of thy strength.

    But thou art brought low.

And I — I did not use my sword or my lance,
With my bare hands I brought about thy downfall.
Of the two of us, is it not I that am the lion?'

And the men hidden behind the rocks shuddered and said, 'Which of us would dare to attack this youth? Prudence demands we abandon our plan and return whence we came.' And this they did, and when 'Antar returned with his flocks and his lion's skin, they joined in the rejoicing at his exploit and appeared as friendly and as deeply impressed as Zuhair himself.

So when, in a few days, the elders of the tribe and the fighting men went off upon a desert raid, Sheddad repented his harshness and left 'Antar, of whom he was secretly proud, in charge of his tents and of the flocks and of the women, and he warned 'Antar not to let any of them wander far, and 'Antar answered proudly, 'O my master, should the smallest

42

object be missing on your return, let me, for the remainder of my life, be kept in chains and bondage.'

But when the warriors had departed, and after a few days constrained within the camp the women became bored, and Samiya, wife of Sheddad, proposed that a feast should be held on the shores of Dhat al Arsad's pools, not far from the camp, and 'Antar dared not hinder her, and indeed rejoiced with the women, for he would be for a whole day in 'Abla's company.

When the pleasure-seekers reached the lakeside on the following day, the sun sparkled upon the waters and was not too hot to hinder their preparations. The servants fanned the charcoal to a steady glow, and lambs were put to roast over it; and the two kids, which had been baking overnight buried in clay pots beneath the soil, were uncovered and distributed with rice and leben among the hungry children. Birds sang among the reeds, and the broad beaches of the lake were bright with flowers. Flushed with wine, some among the girls danced for their elders' delight, discarding their veils; and, among them all, 'Abla was the most beautiful.

Then suddenly a cry rang down the valley, 'The Qahtan, the Qahtan!' And seventy horsemen armed to the teeth seemed to pour like a torrent from the crest of the eastern hill down to the waterside. Each horseman seized one of the girls or the women, and the children scattered, and the servants fled. And 'Antar? As he saw his beloved seized by one of the armed men and dragged to the saddle, 'Antar sprang like a panther and threw the marauder to the dust where death welcomed him as her own. 'Antar seized the warrior's arms and his horse, and pausing only to shelter 'Abla behind some rocks, outstripped the raiders and faced them, crying: 'A curse upon you, evil ones, who dare only to attack women, the daughters and the wives of noble men. Now must you reckon with 'Antar!' Twenty men fell to his lance and sword, and the remainder fled, calling to each other, 'If the slaves of this tribe display such strength and courage, what can the warriors be like!' So the women were saved and returned to camp, praising 'Antar with smiles and tears of gratitude, and 'Antar himself drove before him the arms and the horses of the twenty-one raiders he had slain, and he was elated, remembering 'Abla's heart-felt thanks at her rescue. Only Samiya feared the wrath of Sheddad, her husband, at having so wantonly exposed the tribeswomen to danger, so she swore all to secrecy; and only

'Abla and 'Antar remembered what looks had passed between them after the encounter.

But after a few days, when the warriors also had returned to the camp, Sheddad noticed the twenty-one new horses among his own horses, and he reproached 'Antar unjustly with having organized some raiding party of his own instead of minding the womenfolk — so winning for his tribe the slur of trouble-making. And 'Antar, bound by his promise, gritted his teeth and bore upon his body the whipping his father inflicted, and in his mind the humiliation he so little deserved. But Samiya's heart melted towards him, and in confessing all she saved him further punishment and, indeed, won for him Sheddad's good opinion, for he thought, In truth I have a noble son who has saved all the women of the tribe from rapine and who has allowed himself to suffer unjustly rather than betray a promise. Sheddad rewarded 'Antar with presents, as did the lord Zuhair. And Samiya praised 'Antar in poetry, saying:

'It is right that I respect him, that I protect him,
For did not his strength and valour preserve my honour,
    His courage preserve honour among us all?'

'Antar replied with a poem of gratitude, describing also his own steadfastness, for, he said:

'Men are of two kinds — those whose hearts
Crack with fear as a glass goblet crazes in the heat,
    And those whose hearts are of rock.'

So was Sheddad charmed, as 'Abla had been charmed by a poem on her gaiety and beauty on the day of the picnic by the lake.

The Fifth Story
ABJER THE HORSE

As the months passed, 'Antar's love for 'Abla grew, and his poems were heard by many in the camp and were repeated in the tribe both for their beauty as poems and for their interest, for it was not often that a slave dared to address himself to the daughter of a prince. And 'Abla treasured the poems and learned them. And Sheddad no longer feared his son's exploits, but admired his skills, and now was 'Antar no longer given shepherd's work but went forth with the raiding parties to challenge the enemy tribes and to protect the neighbouring tribes, and he fought with skill and courage — but always as a slave, with no horse or weapons of his own. And still Rabia hated and feared the black upstart who seemed to be making such sure headway into the affections of Zuhair and the Prince and all the people.

At about this time, moreover, the young coxcomb, Amara, brother of Rabia, became enamoured of 'Abla, and he sensed the feelings she began to admit towards the author of those poems, for in the Arab mind no person stands higher in merit than the true poet, to whom words are as jewels to string upon a necklace. Time after time was 'Antar rewarded at the tribal feasts and assemblies for his prowess in battle or his prowess in poetry, and now within the tribes he had many friends and only a few bitter enemies. 'Abla's mother, Sheriya, began to understand 'Antar's love for her daughter, and she challenged him to speak of this love openly and in poetry, so 'Antar spoke thus:

'How lovely is the damsel who has scarred my heart
  With her eyes' arrows;
These precious wounds will never heal.

She passes by, running to the pastures with the other girls,
  They are like gazelles,
But their glances, too, are like javelins.
She strolls by, and I murmur, this is the branch of an erak
  tree,
    Supple in the wind.

She sees me then, and I murmur, here is a wild doe, timid,
  Watching for danger in the desert.
But she smiles, and I see pearls gleaming between her lips,
  Red as the wild cyclamen of the hilltops, wet with rain.

She kneels before the grandeur of her God, and I believe
  The lesser gods lean forward, straining their eyes,
    To see her beauty.'

Sheriya was charmed by 'Antar's verses, and 'Abla too, and
the poems were much repeated and admired. But the coxcomb
Amara became more and more vexed since he could not bear to
think of a black slave admiring 'Abla, and her brother Amr also
was vexed. And he plotted to kill 'Antar, but such was
'Antar's strength and his courage that he foiled several
ambushes with ease; and Shiboob, his half-brother, proved a
useful ally, for he had friends among all the servants and his
knowledge of the tribe was as great as his knowledge of the
desert itself.

So it came about that 'Antar's prestige grew and he achieved
a double triumph when he rescued 'Abla, and her mother, and
her mother's maid-servants from a further raid against them as
they were journeying to a wedding party celebrated some three
days from the Abs camp. 'Antar's triumph was this: not only
did he save his beloved by warding off a host of forty horsemen, but in the few moments before the clash of arms, Sheriya
cried to 'Antar, 'Save us, we beg of you, from these armed and
wicked men.' And 'Antar found time to bargain with her, and
he said, 'O Sheriya, I love your daughter 'Abla with a passion
excelling even the heat of the noonday sun in the long and
weary summer months, and I beg of you to allow me to ask for
her hand. If I can be assured of your support in this enterprise,
I will willingly pit my strength and my wits against these

rascals in your defence, and in 'Abla's.' Sheriya hastily agreed to his conditions, and when the fight was over, and 'Abla once more safe from danger, she herself called to her defender, 'May God reward you, with your dark visage and your noble and enlightened heart.' And Zuhair heaped presents upon 'Antar, as did Malec and Sheriya, and jealousy and hatred grew in the hearts of Rabia, Amara the Coxcomb, and Amr, 'Abla's brother.

Then did Sheriya speak to Malec of 'Antar's love for their daughter 'Abla, and Malec said to her simply, 'However noble his actions may have been, how can such a union take place, between our daughter and a base-born slave, a Negro at that?' And 'Antar spoke to his mother, Zebeeba, of his parentage, but when her son told of his love for his cousin, she said, 'However noble your actions may have been, how can such a union take place between their daughter and a base-born slave, a Negro at that?'

Yet 'Antar in his new-found confidence approached Sheddad when all had been feasting with the sheikh and many were drunk with good wine. And he said to Sheddad, 'O my father, today I have brought triumph and safety to the tribe, and I have learned of my exalted parentage, and I beg of you most humbly to acknowledge me as your son so that I may take my rightful place with the warriors of the tribe; and so that there may be no bar to my union with 'Abla whom I am proud at last to call my cousin, and whom I love.' But Sheddad was angered by the request, and fell upon 'Antar as before, lashing at him with blows which 'Antar suffered in silence and humility out of respect and love for his father. But later, in an agony of shame and resentment, he sought out his friend the Prince, despairing of recognition and weeping bitterly. The Prince comforted 'Antar, but advised him that he had been too precipitate in his approach to his father, and that he had been rash to speak of his love, for 'Abla would now be closely kept and Sheddad might well plot against his turbulent son, together with Rabia and Amara and Amr, whose designs on 'Antar's life had hitherto been unsuccessful. The two friends wept together, 'Antar confessing that it was only for love of 'Abla that he desired nobility — and before dawn, drenched with grief as the pastures are drenched with dew at the turn of the year, 'Antar set out into the desert alone, leaving even Shiboob behind him.

When day dawned he found himself far from the camp, and he rejoiced to be rid of all human companionship, for it seemed to him that men conspired against him. And a day passed, and night followed, and late on the second day he fell in with a company of forty horsemen, and these horsemen knew him by reputation as a gallant fighter and an Arab at heart. They were men of the Abs tribe and their leader was Gheyad ibn Nakhib. 'Come,' they said to 'Antar, 'ally yourself with us in our raids against Qahtan who have done great mischief to our people and to your people alike.' And 'Antar joined with them, for they treated him as an equal and a noble warrior, and not as a slave. And his new friends assessed his strength and decided he should, as a stranger, retain only a quarter-share of any prize; but as his great power and skill was revealed to them, they increased his proportion of their booty to a half-share, a slave's half-share, and then to two thirds, for, they said, ' 'Antar deserves perhaps even more than this since, happen what may, he is a noble fellow, and not everyone who is called a warrior is truly a warrior.' So 'Antar with his friends raided deep in to Qahtan territory.

But it happened that one day 'Antar was separated from his companions and found himself attacked by a grave young man of dignified appearance, riding upon a colt of superlative beauty; and together the two young men skirmished, and they fought and rode far into the desert, yet would the grave young man never engage in close combat but seemed always to avoid 'Antar and entice him further into the wilderness. As they rode 'Antar became enchanted, as with a sorcerer's spell, by the qualities of the horse upon which the grave stranger rode. For here was a horse black as the night sky, yet polished like a basalt stone from Mafraq. His ears were straight, and pricked like a reed pen; his nostrils flared like those of the true Arab breed, beautiful as the black petals of an iris from Madiba. Straight were his legs, and rounded his body and haunches; his tail and mane flowed like the midnight wind, and his hooves lay flat and neat and round like coins upon the sand. Intelligence gleamed in his eye, and when he whinnied it was as though he were speaking.

So 'Antar called to the rider of the colt, and he arranged a parley, and because they were men of a kind, trust and love grew between them and 'Antar learned that the grave young man was none other than Harith, son of Obad, and a guest among the Qahtan whom he wished, therefore, to help to regain the spoils won from them by the men of Abs. And such was the nobility of Harith that, like a true Arab, he was prepared to bargain his dearest possession to regain the possessions of his hosts. So was the bargain struck, and 'Antar, greatly admiring this liberal-minded stranger, exchanged horses with him, agreeing to return all which had been won from the Qahtan. And the name of the colt was Abjer, and his breeding was by Wasil out of Hamama.

Now while Harith and 'Antar were tightening the girths of the two horses, Harith explained how he had never allowed Abjer within reach of an enemy's sword, so as to preserve him. And 'Antar marvelled at the sensitivity of Harith. Then the riders of Gheyad caught up with the two young men, and 'Antar explained to them the nobility of Harith's offer and directed them to return to the Qahtan all the prizes they had recently won from them. But they muttered among themselves, 'Abjer is doubtless a colt of supreme value, and yet what is there in this bargain for us?' Yet they agreed, remarking 'Antar's threatening appearance on his black steed, and the confident strength of Harith, and the love apparent between the two. Then Harith rode off with the cattle and flocks captured by Gheyad, to return these to his hosts, the Qahtan.

As for the Abs they were to some extent rewarded, for on the next raid, which was directed against men escorting a bride, Amina, to her wedding, 'Antar allowed them to keep some of the gifts she carried with her, and the horses and camels. He himself took charge of the bride and her maid-servants, but did them no harm in honour of his love for 'Abla. And Amina's story is told among the tribes to this day, and we may hear it still. But when his part was played, 'Antar now left his friends and devoted himself to Abjer, finding him, as Harith has said, 'a colt beyond price, the envy of Chosroes and of Caesar and the Grecian kings'; a colt which could skim over the stony desert as a hawk skims, seeming to touch the ground only with his shadow.

When he returned to camp after several days, all were amazed at his marvellous steed. Zebeeba, indeed, reproached him for his interest in raiding and fighting, but 'Antar only smiled, and he was welcomed in Samiya's tents to tell his story, and refresh his spirits by a glimpse of 'Abla in all her modesty and gentleness. And at the lord Zuhair's feast, too, he was welcome, for tempers had cooled in his absence, and Sheddad could not but admire the horse Abjer.

The Sixth Story
AMINA BINT YEZID

Now the Abs tribe, while a powerful and wealthy people, rich above all in the nobility and courage of their leader the lord Zuhair, were but one among many neighbouring tribes, and among these was the great tribe of Tai. And the ruler of the Taians was Handala, Prince among Princes, he that was known as the 'Blood-drinker', so many had been the victims of his wrath and his raids. And his tribe was famous for its brave men and fair women — among them the princess who married a king in Egypt so long ago, and who carried with her into that soft and sunlit land ideas of the One True God whom all were to come to worship in the latter days. The son of Handala was Yezid, and Yezid's daughter Amina was betrothed to Nakid ibn Jella of the Ma'ani people.

Amina was journeying to join her future husband. She travelled in a palanquin, and at the time of our story this was attacked by the men with whom 'Antar had thrown in his lot in the desert, consumed as he was by misery and frustration, for it seemed to him in those days that he would never achieve either recognition in his own tribe or success in his desire for betrothal with his fair cousin 'Abla. So he fought alongside Gheyad's men, though it was not his custom to attack the escorts of women, and from the first he was determined to save Amina from the clutches of his wild and outcast comrades.

Amina was escorted by maid-servants and by seventy men, and of these ten fled, five to the left and five to the right; and five of these men escaped to warn Nakid ibn Jella of his bride's

51

danger, and five to warn Yezid ibn Handala of his daughter's peril. And 'Antar and his men slaughtered Amina's escort and seized the considerable riches with which she was endowed.

Now Gheyad and his men were already angry with 'Antar after he had forced them to return much bounty to the Qahtan tribe in payment for the courtesy of Harith, who had allowed 'Antar to possess himself of the wondrous horse Abjer, prized by Harith above all his possessions. Anyone could see that Harith and 'Antar were men of a kind, and that love and trust had grown between them when the bargain was struck; and Harith, in the Arab manner, sacrificed his own prize to regain the lost cattle and flocks of his Qahtan hosts. But thereafter Gheyad and his raiders, who were less noble in their outlook than the great 'Antar and the grave young Harith, reproached themselves for giving in so easily to the superiority of the two leaders, saying to themselves, 'It is not just that we have been deprived of our due; and noble as the motives of 'Antar and his friend Harith may be, can we afford to move in such exalted company?' From which it may be seen that Gheyad and his men were low fellows, outcasts, not altogether worthy of the name of Arab. Moreover, they had quickly forgotten the bargain they had struck with this mighty slave on the matter of dividing spoils won in battle; for since they had recognized his chivalrous qualities, how could it now be possible to relegate his share to that of a slave?

So when Amina and her women sat weeping on the stony ground before them, the raiders, with stony hearts, would have taken both the women and their wealth had not 'Antar once more intervened, saying, 'O my companions, again I must ask that the spoils of this modest affray be divided according to my ideas rather than your own, and this for two reasons. For one, I have borne the brunt of the fighting, and for another, my love for my cousin 'Abla precludes me from molesting this maiden or her attendants. And furthermore,' he added, ignoring the tension which thickened between the women and the men during his discourse, 'it is evident that the bride here is no other than Amina bint Yezid, and her father is no other than Yezid ibn Handala, the Blood-drinker and Prince of Tai. You well know that the Taians are a powerful people and have no particular quarrel with the Abs, and I would not provoke them further, for is it not true what Malik the Prince says to his friends, "Two may make a quarrel, but two hundred may die for it?" Therefore,' he continued to his restless and resentful companions, 'I ask you to entrust Amina and her maidens to my care, and I will see that they remain unscathed, and I will hand them over to the safe-keeping of my lord Zuhair so they may return to Tai. For my love of 'Abla is such,' said 'Antar ominously, yet to the growing delight of Amina and her attendants, 'that I can indeed take no pleasure in any other woman.' So the raiders, aware of 'Antar's great strength and of his firm purpose, had to make do with only a portion of Amina's dowry, and with the horses and accoutrements of the slaughtered men who had been unable to protect her. And 'Antar's presence safeguarded the maidens, though all he did was sit between them and the men, cross-legged upon Abjer his horse, leaning upon his lance and silent as the Colossi in the Egyptian desert, intimidating the dejected raiders by the sheer power of his presence.

But now retribution was to fall upon them all, for a company of the men of Tai, warned by those who had earlier escaped, rode down in a cloud of dust to challenge Amina's captors. And the raiders turned from their silent and resentful encounter with 'Antar to face three hundred horsemen in armour, led by Yezid himself. Yet 'Antar, because of his feelings for Yezid and Amina, would not join in the fight, but sat cross-legged still upon his black horse, his sword sheathed, mute and still in the uproar. Then, as he watched, he saw his friends were in deep trouble and resolved to help them, so for the first time he spoke to Abjer, saying, 'Now, Abjer, must we join in battle with our friends.'

Now Abjer was a horse bred and born to battle for the right, and the voice of his master was as the voice of God to him. For Abjer was an ancestor of that horse of whom the tale is told that, when the Prophet himself — blessed be he — was lost in the desert with a few followers, and thirsty withal, the horses smelled water and raced to the water's brink. Yet as they raced a bugle blew, and one horse, his thirst unquenched, returned obedient to his master lest his services be needed. And from this horse of the Prophet — upon whom be peace — were descended those whose riders spread the True Faith to the ends of the earth itself. So Abjer thrust forward into the fight as a man thrusts through his prison doors to freedom; and as he swept towards the enemy, Abjer's own voice arose over the roar of battle in a resonant neighing, and at the sound the steeds of the enemy shrank back in fear, unhorsing many of their riders, so that Gheyad's men took heart and fell upon the Taians, though many of these escaped in the confusion, including Amina's father, Yezid.

Then came Gheyad to 'Antar, saying, 'O most excellent warrior, you have restored to us our courage and our honour, and no longer will we seek to demean our comradeship by ignoble disputes about the prizes to be won.' But scarcely had he spoken than a cloud of dust arose on the further quarter, and Nakid's men swept down upon them, five thousand strong, and Nakid himself led them, black with anger like a ghoul from the burial grounds. And 'Antar's companions fled before the wrath of these men of Ma'an, but 'Antar stood his ground and challenged Nakid, their leader, to single combat.

Now it happened that at home in the Abs camp, the lord Zuhair was greatly worried by the difficulties between Sheddad and his adventurous son 'Antar. And Zuhair called to Sheddad to reason with him, and he spoke to him of 'Antar's great qualities, and Zuhair embraced Sheddad and begged him to take a more generous and a more reasonable view. Now was Sheddad moved by Zuhair's interest in his son, yet had he to tell Zuhair that he was powerless to effect a reconciliation since 'Antar had stormed off into the desert alone. So Zuhair sent for his sons and his leaders and a search was made, and thus it came about that the Prince met in the desert with the raiders who had deserted 'Antar and learned from them that he was locked in mortal combat with Nakid ibn Jella, alone against five thousand men. And the Prince spurred his swift horse, and his men followed at speed, so that they topped the ridge just in time to see 'Antar fell his opponent before all the men of Ma'an. Whereupon the Ma'an host fled leaderless, and the Prince and 'Antar embraced as equals. And they set off home together.

But Amina wept with her maidens, for although she recognized her debt to 'Antar in preserving them all from the rapacity of the desert raiders, she had nevertheless lost her husband and half her dowry, and had seen her father fly defeated from the battlefield. Yet she was comforted by the courtesy which 'Antar and the Prince accorded her in her misery. And as they rode home 'Antar sang of his own love:

'I have seen her there, seated upon silk cushions,
Milk white she is, as the cool milk I bring her at dawn,
    Her breasts rose-tipped as the dawn.
Yet her long hair curtains her from my sight,
      Dark as night
Falls her long hair like dark clouds masking the break of day.

    All who see her are ravished by her beauty,
      All flock to see her, are intoxicated
    With their good fortune, with the delight
Of watching, of admiring, of comparing her perfections.

   — Yet I — I must hide my love, bury it deep in my heart,
    Until, O God, it may be that my fortunes change.'

And the Prince, delighted, cried, 'O 'Antar, you have attained full mastery not only over men, but over words; indeed you are skilled in poetry.'

'Antar's return was an occasion for feasting which lasted for three days, and which ended with 'Antar proclaiming his love for 'Abla in a poem of such beauty that Zuhair asked Shas, who was skilled in these things, to write it down. Yet Shas was jealous, and sought to lower 'Antar in his lord's eyes; but Zuhair said, 'Envy has no part to play in the character of a noble man.' And Shas was silenced. Then Zuhair demanded of 'Antar why he had been absent so long, to which the young man replied, 'My lord, I am but a slave, and a slave must learn to bear anger without animosity. But one night I was drunk, and in my drunkenness I demanded of my master a favour of which I am unworthy. So I was obliged to leave the tribe. But now I am returned to beg forgiveness.' And, seeing Sheddad approach at this moment, he turned to him, crying with great feeling, 'O my master, I would say to you as the poet says, here come I as one who may deserve blame, but yet have pity upon a servant who craves your pardon!'

And all could recognize that it was not fear which brought 'Antar so humbly before his father, but love; which tames all and renders gentle the hearts even of the most powerful. And all rejoiced in the reconciliation of 'Antar and Sheddad.

The Seventh Story
RECOGNITION

Now summer gripped the desert and the camp, and all live things panted beneath the sun's mastery, and men and women laboured in the early morning or the cool of the evening. Sheddad left the camp overnight because he heard that Qais, son of Dhobian, had swept from the Yemen with forty horsemen to plunder the Hejaz, and that because of the great heat he would be resting by the pools of flowing water in the oasis of Douma. So Sheddad went out to raid the raider, and after one day 'Antar followed with Shiboob his brother, who warned him of another plot against his life. By the waterside they found and tended a wounded man, who described a great fight between the two parties and told them to their grief that Sheddad had been injured in this fight. After binding up his wounds, which they dressed with oil and a little wine, 'Antar and Shiboob left their friend in the shade of the reeds by the waterside where he would be safe, and hurried on.

Sure enough, they caught up with the two bands of men, still fighting and struggling in the desert, with the hot dust billowing over them and the silver of swords flashing within the dust and the sand soaked red with blood. Then did 'Antar plunge into the combat, and he brought his sword down upon the head of Qais, who rode upon a white horse, and the sword sliced through the man and through his saddle and through the horse itself so that the four pieces lay upon the ground and all were astounded.

And 'Antar shouted in triumph:

'I long for the blows of cleaving scimitars,
I worship the thrust of a well-fashioned spear.

    I welcome the cup of death,
      The pure liquid,
The blow, the thrust, the horse stumbling among
    death-bearing lances under a pall of dust,
      Under the wings of darkness.

I am alone with the dust and the shadows
Coursing over the desert as the storms do,
As the salukis do, following their prey.

I watch for the glimmer of lances in the dimness,
The flash of steel like stars sparkling,
Like lightning in the dark of the night.

    O by my life,
Honour and glory and fame are for him who hurls
    himself into battle with a pure heart,
In battle are the highest honours to be won.
Let him fight with a firm heart, let him wield his sword
    and spear undaunted by calamity,
Or else lead a life of ignominy with no reward
    from the maidens, and no mourning
From his friends when he must die.

I am a hero well remembered for my battles,
An eager knight, an equal among my peers,
A wolf assaulting the camps, a lion defending my tribe
    and my friends.'

So sang 'Antar, and so did he save his wounded father, but
his sword was broken with the blow.

Now it happened that the men of Abs returned victorious to
their camp, and 'Antar rode ahead of his companions and
came upon two men, one of whom was searching and digging
in the sand of a small wadi while the other, his brother, lay in
the shade of the oleander bushes, watching him with a
malicious eye. And as 'Antar rode up the younger man gave a
cry of delight and from the sand drew a sword whose black
blade glowed darkly in the sunlight. And the elder man leaped
from the cool shadows and fell upon his brother, and would
have slain him had not 'Antar killed him first, determined to

defend the weaker of the two. And the young man, whose name was Nizar, son of Bassam, son of Osama, told 'Antar this story:

'My grandfather, Osama, son of Teba, owned many camels, and once he journeyed in the desert with his camels and herdsmen and one camel strayed from the flock, and a herdsboy picked up a black, sparkling stone from the desert sand and flung it at the camel, meaning to urge it on the path of its fellows. But the stone hurtled through the camel's body, emerging at speed on the further side, and the camel fell dead. And Osama found the rock from which the stone had chipped, and he brought it to his father Teba. And Teba found a blacksmith who could fashion a sword from this rock, which had perhaps fallen from the stars at night. And when the sword was finished, Teba sheathed it in a scabbard of leather and gold, but the blacksmith he slew. And the sword came in turn to Osama, his son, and to Bassam, my father,' said Nizar. 'Now my father neither liked nor trusted his eldest son, whom you have just slain, so, on his deathbed, he gave me charge of the sword and bade me take it to Nushirvan, king of Persia, or to some emperor in the West, who would reward me handsomely, "For," he said, "such a sword is worthy of princes, and we would benefit more from the wealth it would bring to our tribe." So I buried the sword to preserve it from the malice of my brother, who would not respect the wishes even of his dead father — and he forced me back here to look for the sword. He had already despoiled me of my father's inheritance, leaving me nothing but a rope's end. He was a despicable man and unworthy of the name Arab. Now, O my generous and gallant rescuer, I can return and claim my inheritance; but my father's sword will I leave with you, for have you not saved me from destruction and my tribe from dishonour under an ignoble leader? Moreover,' continued the younger brother, 'I foresee that you will one day be as great and powerful as Nushirvan himself.'

'Antar buckled on the sword, which was called Dami, and he saw that Nizar was well rewarded from the plunder of subsequent raids. 'Antar returned to the camp, riding proudly upon Abjer, his black horse, and armed with Dami, his black sword, and well content in the love and gratitude of his father Sheddad.

On his return, 'Antar learned that Amara the Coxcomb had

approached Malec, demanding the hand of his daughter 'Abla, for Amara had heard 'Antar's poems describing 'Abla, and his ears had fallen in love before his eyes. But Malec rather despised Amara's extravagance and vanity, his scented hair, his white-faced horse and his fine clothing, and had as yet made no firm decision. And 'Antar swore to himself, 'By the one eternal God, the God of Abraham and of Moses, he will not have her!'

But later it happened that Malec relented, and a betrothal was arranged, for Amara had pressed his claims and had ascertained through a maid-servant that 'Abla was indeed as beautiful as the moon, and not without riches. So 'Antar came in anguish to the Prince, and the Prince, to save 'Abla, claimed her as his own, meaning to keep her safe in his own tents until Sheddad should acknowledge 'Antar as a worthy member of the tribe; for the Prince loved 'Antar and would not see 'Abla wedded to a member of the Zaiyad such as Rabia or Amara. But Sheddad could not bring himself to take this step, and moreover, for all the Prince's pleading, he sent 'Antar back to look after the flocks; and now we see Amara rejoicing at his good fortune and crowing like a cock at the luck of his clan, the Zaiyad, and Rabia also rejoicing. But 'Abla was in tears, and 'Antar's grief and rage were beyond description. And his grief was exacerbated because his mother had hinted of 'Abla's growing love for him, and the thought of her suffering if married to Amara the Coxcomb drove him to a frenzy. So he fretted his heart out on the far pastures, high on the slopes of Mount Sa'adi, and his brothers Shiboob and Jarir comforted him as best they could. And among the leaders of the tribe and in the lord Zuhair's company the question was debated.

But 'Antar's faithful love and manly virtues were to be rewarded, and this was the way of it. Zuhair heard from his scouts that the tribe of Tai were, after all, up in arms against the Abs people, and he went out to meet them at the head of his armies, and their path led over the high slopes of Mount Sa'adi. And here was a terrible battle fought between the Taians and the Absians, and the Taians were the stronger. And Sheddad, fighting on the flank, looked up from the turmoil and saw his son 'Antar and the two brothers, mounted yet motionless, apart from the fighting, like standing stones. He cried to them to help him, but 'Antar answered, 'Nay, master,

I am but a slave and am not fit to mingle with warriors, the nobility of the tribe of Abs.' Again Sheddad, and Malec too, pleaded with him, but 'Antar called back to them, 'What can you ask of me? Whoever dreamed of asking protection and countenance from a slave?' And a third time Sheddad groaned to him in desperation from the battlefield, with Malec and Rabia adding their fervent entreaties, and at last 'Antar responded, 'O my master, you are my father too, and I will help you, and I will help my fellow tribesmen, but first must you assure me of my rightful place among the knights, for I am of noble blood and would take my place among equals under our lord Zuhair; and I would, when the battle is over, be recognized as a worthy suitor, O Malec, for the hand of your daughter, my cousin 'Abla.' And, as may be imagined, the three hard-pressed warriors agreed to these demands on the instant, and in a flash 'Antar and his brothers descended upon the enemy. Some said it was as though three dust-devils had whirled into the fight, and others likened them to a wall of rock separating from the mountainside and scattering the enemy under the weight of its fall.

Then the men of Tai fled, defeated, though a party of horsemen dashed through the Abs camp, enabling Yezid, their leader, to guide his daughter Amina safely through the battle to freedom. And the lord Zuhair led his men home in triumph, each one being laden with booty. And on their return the feasting lasted for seven days, and 'Antar was overwhelmed with rich presents.

Sheddad now made up his mind to fulfil the promises made to his valiant son. So, at a meeting of the tribe's elders, he announced to the whole assembly, 'O my brothers, 'Antar by his great deeds has rendered himself worthy to inherit my rank, and I may no longer refuse to recognize him as my son. I ask you all to accept him as a worthy member of our tribe.' Whereupon Shas cried furiously, 'Are you mad, cousin, to share your nobility with a slave? Has any Arabian sanctioned this hitherto?' But Zuhair silenced him, saying, 'O Shas, I have no regard for the envious — who are you to judge between a father and his son? Sheddad must do with 'Antar as he desires, and I strongly commend this decision.' And Amr, brother of 'Abla, added, 'O 'Antar, never would I have allowed my sister to marry a slave, a herder of camels, but today, since you stand among us as free and as noble as your father, you are worthy also to take my sister in betrothal. Remember me hereafter, I pray you, as your humble servant.'

Then 'Antar at last took his rightful place in the assembly, for was not his father Sheddad, the son of Karad, for all that his mother was a captive slave? And all rejoiced at the coming happiness of 'Antar and 'Abla. But despite his honeyed words, Amr still hated and despised 'Antar; and Shas, with Rabia and Amara, hated and feared him too. And they plotted against the hero, furious at his success and yet afraid both of his virtues and of his courage.

The Eighth Story
HASSAN AND HIS LOVE

Now among the sons of Zuhair, the noble and
generous leader of the tribe, Malik the Prince was the most
loved for his good humour and his serenity, and it was clear
that he inherited from his mother, Temadhur, the skill and
insight by which he was sometimes able to persuade his fellow
men to settle their disputes by means other than force.
Temadhur, when her son Malik was newly born, had handed
him over to the care of a slave attendant upon her, and this
slave's name was Leila, and she was the widow of Harith the
Mazeni; and Leila's own son, Hassan, and Temadhur's son,
Malik, were suckled at the same breast.

So Hassan and Malik grew up as milk brothers; played as
children together, and as boys trained in the skills they would
need as men. Leila and Temadhur loved and compared the
two boys as they grew into manhood, and between the two
women was perfect understanding and the love of equals, for
such is the way of the Arabs with their slaves and servants.
Leila would wait upon Temadhur, bringing her water daily
and combing her lovely hair, and she also washed and tended
and soothed the two lads, her own and his milk brother,
warmly aware of the close bonds existing between them all
four.

Now it happened one day that there was a stir in the camp
and all were amazed to see, afar off, a lone woman riding upon
a lame horse which stumbled towards the shelter of the
encampment. The woman slipped down from the saddle, and

having asked for assistance and succour for her ailing steed, begged to be taken before Temadhur, wife of Zuhair, whom she had come from afar to petition. So, when she had been given water and a clean robe, the woman was brought before Temadhur, and with Temadhur were her attendants, among them Leila, the servant; but the boys were now of an age to be away in the desert, and only the smaller children were playing and calling outside the tents.

The woman approached Temadhur and said, 'O most noble lady, I am Hind, and I come from the Mazen country, and all these years I have yearned to see again the sister whom I loved: Leila who, men tell me, has been in your service so long. And I am come to beg of you to free my sister so that I can take her to her own people, to live with them and with me.' At this Leila was moved to leave her mistress's side, and she threw herself into the arms of her sister Hind who had come so far and braved so many dangers to seek her and perhaps to bring her home. And Temadhur was touched by the love the sisters bore each other, and she ordered a feast among the women, and it was not long before she saw that she must give up her beloved maid and allow her to return to Mazen country with her sister Hind.

So Leila and Hind set off on their long journey, and soon Hassan became accustomed to travelling between his own tribe and his adopted tribe; and Malik, the young Prince, would visit his milk brother, to whom he was devoted, and Hassan would visit him in return.

Now Hassan's father, Harith, had died at the time of his wife's capture in days when the Abs and the Mazen peoples were at war, so Hassan's mother and his aunt were by no means wealthy members of their tribe — in fact it had been in the hope of finding her sister to be mother of a strong young lad who could help them all that Hind had set out across the desert in the first place. And the three of them now lived in some poverty, though they were loved and revered by the tribe. Hassan was a handsome young man, and it was easy for him to win the hearts of the Mazen maidens to whom he could tell stories of his life in a far-off country. So when he courted Nahima, daughter of Nejem, a leader of the tribe, she loved him. But Nejem favoured the advances of Awef ibn Alkem of the Terjemid peoples, and at a feast, when the Mazeni men were making merry with guests from among the Terjemids, the two suitors clashed. 'For all I have lost my father,' cried Hassan, 'I am strong and young and worthy to marry Nahima, whom I love. Moreover, it is clear,' he added, 'that she herself prefers my company to yours.' 'Nay, you lie,' retorted Awef. 'You are but an exile, and numbered among the herd of orphans.' At this Hassan became angrier than ever, for it was true that, because of his absence as a child, his father's property had returned to the tribe, this being the Arab custom of inheritance, and children who have not laboured for their people have no real claim on that people's wealth. Hassan threw himself upon Awef, and the two men fought before all the assembly, while Nahima prayed to Lat and Uzza for Hassan's victory.

Now the fight ended well, and Hassan was poised to kill Awef, but he relented because Awef was a guest of the Mazen people, and thereupon, in his moment of triumph, Hassan left his loved one, and his enemy, and his people, determined to win flocks and herds for himself. With a few friends and their swift horses, he rode off into the desert to redeem his fortune.

At this time a great famine came upon the countries bordering the grazing lands of the Mazen, and the Qahtan, led by Osakh, issued forth from the dry pastures which could no longer support their camels nor their sheep. The sun beat fiercely upon the raiders as they rode, and a hot wind from the east blew before it whorls of dust, and the lightly pricking tangles of camel-thorn goaded the horses into uneasiness. Later the wind dropped and the horses smelled water, and the riders could see a silver mirage with figures moving, and as they slowed to a stealthy walk they came, amazed, upon a scene of great beauty, a glimpse of paradise. For before them lay a sheet of dimpling water, blue and silver and edged with soft green grass and desert flowers, both white and orange; and piled upon the daisies and the tiny marigolds lay the cottons and gay silks and velvets of a dozen lovely maidens who splashed and swam in the cool ripples beyond a barrier of reeds. Loveliest among them all as they played naked in the water was Nahima, and Osakh determined then to conquer her as he hoped to conquer the Mazen and take their wealth from them.

Yet would he first try to win her by consent, and so, still hidden by the reeds, he and his men veered off as quietly as they had come to the lakeside; and approaching the near-by

'*A dozen lovely maidens who splashed and swam in the ripples*'

camp they claimed audience with Nejem and the **other** leaders. Then Osakh demanded Nahima's hand in marriage.

'This cannot be,' said Nejem, 'for my daughter is already betrothed to Hassan ibn Harith, and already he has proved himself man enough to defend what is her own choice. Nor can I believe,' he added, comparing the emaciated horses and travel-stained visitors with his own well-fed warriors, 'that Nahima would wish to transfer her affections elsewhere.' At this Osakh's rage mounted within him, and he cursed Nejem and he cursed Hassan, and he swore to annihilate the Mazen people, whom he infuriated further by revealing how he and his men had enjoyed at least a glimpse of the Mazen women in their privacy. And rage thickened between the two groups of warriors as Osakh wheeled his raiders into the wind and galloped off to seek reinforcements.

When the girls returned to the camp they were greeted by a stream of blistering oaths from their mothers and aunts, and upbraided for the carelessness which had led to such grave impropriety, and which indeed might even imperil the survival of the Mazen tribe, for the Qahtan were a powerful enemy. It was useless for Nahima to plead with her mother that the little look-out girl they had posted to warn them of an approach of strangers had been tempted herself to strip and splash among the reeds. 'It is evident, Nahima,' cried her mother, 'that you have no more sense than a young owl in the sunshine, putting your honour thus in the hands of a ten-year-old.' And she beat her daughter severely, marring the smooth thighs with red scars; and when Hassan returned next day, triumphant with a wealth of cattle and many fine camels, Nahima's eyes also were red, with weeping.

But Hassan and the warriors calculated that before the Qahtan returned there would be time for the marriage feasting, and Nahima dried her eyes and donned her cottons and silks and velvets, and her friends combed and oiled and polished her hair and decked it with daisies and tiny marigolds and dark salvia, and her mother rubbed away the whipping stripes with a precious unguent, and so Nahima and Hassan were safely wed.

Then the scouts came with news that the Qahtan were truly on the march, and not only they, but with them Zaker, Anka, Masud ibn Messad el Kelbi, the Beni Asad and the Beni Rhani. So Hassan rose from his marriage bed, chose a hundred men and set off in a storm of dust for the pools of Dhat al Arsad; and Hassan shouted as he passed the tent where the leaders were conferring: 'Never fear, I will return with Prince Malik, my milk brother, and with a thousand warriors of the Abs, and we will crush these vipers of Qahtan!' And the dark figures disappeared into the dark night.

After two days Hassan rode up to the lakeside where the Prince was encamped with all his men, and the Prince embraced Hassan and learned first of his love and marriage, and then of the plight which had fallen upon his tribe because of famine and because of his true love's careless impropriety: and the Prince rallied to Hassan, crying, 'Now may I prove the bond which binds us and the love which unites us as brothers.' And 'Antar, remembering perhaps the day with 'Abla by another lakeside, swore to follow the Prince in support of his friend. And after three days the army set off, a thousand strong and armed with steel and with cuirasses. But 'Antar went by a different route, and it was thus, some men say, that he came upon the two brothers fighting over the sword Dami which was said to have fallen as a stone from the stars at night, and been wrought by a blacksmith who was himself slain by Teba abu Osama. And the sword was sheathed in a scabbard of leather and gold, and when drawn for the slaying it glowed darkly in the sunlight and was indeed a sword worthy of princes. 'Antar had clashed with the men of Qais ibn Dhobian from the Yemen, he who wounded Sheddad himself; and with the Prince of Tai in the high slopes of Mount Sa'adi; and with Gheidac, an ally of Osakh's, who was attacking 'Antar's friends. And this was Gheidac whom men hated for his haughtiness and yet despised since he had delayed in avenging his father, whom 'Antar had previously killed. Thus it was that 'Antar came almost too late to save Hassan and the Prince and the men who had but lately set off a thousand strong and armed with steel and with cuirasses; for Osakh was a valiant fighter, and his enemies were sorely pressed when 'Antar came to their aid.

The great dark figure plunged into the conflict, and was almost lost in the dust of it, and as he fought he shouted these words through the turmoil:

'See how I turn upon my enemy, enemy of my friends and
   of those who misjudged me.

Who can now reproach me for my dark complexion?
  I glory in my darkness.
Who can reproach me for my humble birth?
  I befriend princes.

Who dares reproach me, dares deride me?
Do they forget how the good draws envy to herself?

Under the One Creator I am self-made, my own deeds and
  my sword have made me.
  Here's my nobility, and here my glory.'

Whereupon he killed Osakh and he killed Gheidac also, and
he left Osakh and his horse in four pieces upon the blood-
soaked sand.

Then the grateful Hassan, with the men of Mazen, escorted
both 'Antar and the Prince, milk brother to Hassan, on their
homeward way; and Hassan later returned unscathed to his
bride, Nahima.

But the Prince himself seemed untouched by the love of
women.

The Ninth Story
THE QUEST

The worst of the dreaded summer heat was abating, and the tiny white clouds of autumn chased across the wearisome blue of the sky, their shadows drifting below them over the many-coloured slopes and flats of the desert, and over the salt sands where none may pass; and now both men and women looked forward to the promise of rain and of pasture for the flocks. They remembered the cool relief of winter and the beauty of its flowers and its passing birds. Already heavy dews had brought to life the graceful squills, whose clusters shaded the stony ridges of the hills with their violet drifts when 'Antar and 'Abla were betrothed.* And such was 'Antar's delight that he showered upon Malec many rich robes and vestments won in battle, even in the tent where the ceremony was witnessed; adding, in his enthusiasm, his own silk-embroidered jerkin which he gave to Amr who had wilfully admired it, knowing he must thus receive it as a gift, for such is the Arab way.

And 'Abla admired the dark form of her future husband as he stood there, stripped to the waist, and she both laughed and cried to see the scars and wounds upon his chest and back and arms, for although she was well used to tending the warriors of the tribe when they were wounded, she had never seen such scars, and she thought to herself, I both weep and laugh to see them, for they would surely have killed even the elephants with

*The flower is *Scilla autumnalis*.

69

which my aunt Zebeeba was familiar as a little girl. And 'Antar rejoiced at her sensitivity; but once the betrothal was completed Malec sent his daughter away to that part of the tents where the women dwell alone.

But among certain men bitterness was growing, and frustration, and the four malcontents brought their evil plans to fruition and came to Malec and said, 'Is it not true, cousin, that you have promised your daughter to a Negro bastard who pretends to our company as an equal?' And Malec cried, 'Nay, by the honour of the Arabs, I have done no such thing, only was I forced into this agreement at the time of the Tai attack.' And Rabia said, 'O Malec, my cousin, I will teach you a way whereby you may safeguard your daughter without breaking your oath, and so rid us all of the Negress's son.' And he told Malec that he must demand of 'Antar a brideprice. (Now this was in the dark days before the coming of the Prophet, peace be upon him, when women were still bought and sold in marriage and had, as yet, no dower of their own for a defence against divorce or widowhood.) This brideprice must, Rabia specified, consist of no less than a thousand flying camels, a breed which grazes in the far country around Hira. 'Now Hira is a city under the rule of King Mundhir, vassal to Chosroes, and it is absolutely impossible for any warrior to obtain the flying camels from their jealous master. 'Antar will assuredly be lost beyond all help, even if he survives the desert crossing to such a place. Yet, should he return empty-handed, he will be dishonoured and no fit match for 'Abla, who can then conveniently be betrothed to Amara, my brother.' And this was agreed, and Malec treacherously made his demand of 'Antar publicly, and 'Antar most joyously accepted the challenge to prove his love. He pledged himself, saying before all the tribe, 'I swear in God's name that I will deliver these thousand flying camels, and that moreover each one of them will be laden with jewels and treasures from the East.' And he bade farewell to his mother Zebeeba immediately, although it was already dark and she had retired; and she called out, 'Where are you going, my son, when other men sleep?' He answered, 'Mother, I go to win a brideprice for my cousin 'Abla.' 'How then did your meeting go, with Malec her father?' asked Zebeeba, and he cried, 'Why splendidly!' and called Shiboob to saddle Abjer and a second horse, and together they pressed forwards into the darkness.

'Where are we going?' asked Shiboob. 'Tell me so that I may guide you by the best path.' 'Towards 'Iraq, to Hira, where I may find the flocks of flying camels grazing and bring a thousand of them as a gift for my uncle Malec,' answered 'Antar. Now was Shiboob aghast, and he whispered, 'O my brother, do you not know that Hira is in a very rich country ruled over by the powerful King Mundhir, a vassal of Chosroes himself, and that these famous flying camels are jealously guarded by men of immense valour?' But 'Antar bade him be silent, son of an adulterer as he was, and added, 'I know what I must do, and with God's help I shall accomplish my task.' So when the night ended the dawn greeted the two horsemen as they journeyed north and east, two small specks in the tawny landscape of the desert, two long shadows on the stony track leading towards Hira.

Now on the third day of their travels they met Harith, son of Zuhair and brother of the Prince, and he too was horrified at the object of their journey and begged them to return, telling them of their danger, but they would not. And on the fifth day of their travels they met an old man, a hermit, and he too was horrified at the object of their journey and begged them to return, telling them of their danger, but they would not. The hermit was a wise man who could see into men's hearts, and it was clear to him that 'Antar's honesty prevented him from perceiving the perfidy of his uncles and cousins who had sent him to certain destruction by their devious plotting. So the hermit revealed the stratagem, hoping that 'Antar would abandon his quest, but 'Antar answered simply, 'How can this be? Have I not sworn in God's name, and before all the tribe, to bring the camels home?'

The hermit led them to the banks of a sliding river, so vast and wide that 'Antar and Shiboob could hardly believe in its reality, and here the old man welcomed them to his modest hut. For here he lived, and he would pace about all day upon the sandy verges of the river, murmuring, 'My youth is lost somewhere in these sands and I am searching for it.' He gave them food and drink and shelter, and he told them of King Mundhir's power, and of the wealthy people of Hira, and the beauties of 'Iraq. For this is the country of the two great rivers, of palm trees and shade and fertile gardens where violets grow as big as roses, and roses as big as thornbushes. Here the nightingale and the dove and the bulbul sing among the pomegranate bushes, and the pious hoopoe, messenger between Solomon and Bilqis, flits over the green lawns; while in the cornfields and on the desert's edge partridges join the quails and the chequered sand-grouse and the barred bustard in chattering the praises of God.

The hermit spoke of the flying camels, which turned out not to have wings, as 'Antar and Shiboob had expected, but whose build was such that they seemed nevertheless to fly over the desert on strong legs and velvet feet, making no more noise than does an owl flitting across the silver sands by moonlight. And these camels were the apple of Mundhir's eye.

On the following day, 'Antar stayed with the hermit, but Shiboob disguised himself as a herdsman and walked in to the city of Hira and beyond, and on the green plains surrounding the great city he came upon the flocks of flying camels with their herdsmen, and he marvelled at them. For the camels were of all colours, from white to gold and from gold to copper and so to black. Their trim bodies and humps were rounded and full, their woolly coats were soft as velvet, and they moved to the sound of a thousand bells. As they grazed over the new-sprung grass, each with his long shadow, they resembled a great multi-coloured carpet thrown upon the pasture. And Shiboob spent the day with the camel-herds, for King Mundhir expected no enemy to cross the desert from the west, and in the east Chosroes secured his safety.

At dawn next day 'Antar donned his armour, and he and Shiboob swept down upon the herd like two dust-devils, carrying all before them and roaring as does the desert wind. With no difficulty they separated a thousand flying camels from the herd, and drove these before them over the grass and sandy scrub. But at the sixth hour the brothers saw a vast cloud of dust behind them and knew they were discovered, and that the herdsmen had roused a force of Mundhir's men. So Shiboob herded the camels into a wadi where they might remain hidden, and 'Antar turned to confront a force of a thousand men, led by Numan, son of King Mundhir himself. And the men swept down upon 'Antar like a swarm of locusts, darkening the sky with their spears and their banners and the dust raised by their horses' hooves.

'Antar fought for an hour against Numan and a thousand men, until Abjer stumbled and fell, whereupon 'Antar continued to fight on foot, but he stumbled upon a skull and was

finally overcome. And Shiboob thought him lost, and drove
the camels before him to a cave, where he persuaded a shepherd to confuse the party sent after him to recapture the flock.
And on the following day he rewarded the shepherd, and set
off home, weeping for 'Antar; but he could not take the camels
with him and they were found by King Mundhir's men and
returned to their master.

Meanwhile 'Antar was bound upon his horse and taken
before Numan, and the whole company returned to Hira,
where 'Antar was brought to the king in a camp outside the
city. Here 'Antar was questioned by the king, and he answered
in the form of a poem thus:

'For love of 'Abla have I killed many a slave,
And won the right to bear my sword.

For love of 'Abla have I vanquished many a warrior,
    And conquered noble men.

Yet for love of 'Abla have I fallen into the snare
  set by my sly uncle,

    For at his behest
I have travelled to a country where misfortune awaits me.
Yet have I encountered here,
A just and magnanimous monarch.'

Now King Mundhir was well pleased with 'Antar's story and
his poem, and would have questioned him further, but at that
moment there leaped from among the bushes growing thick
under the date palms a lion, a Khifan lion, as big as a camel;
and the lion stood there, threatening the assembled crowd,
and the king, and Prince Numan. And 'Antar called to the
king, 'Quick, sire, command that my bonds be unloosed so
that I may kill this monster which would kill us all,' and King
Mundhir's men trembled as they loosed 'Antar's hands, thrust-
ing into them his sword Dami; and indeed they were unable
to undo the fetters binding his ankles. But even so 'Antar
triumphed, for, bounding towards the lion with his feet still
shackled, he killed it with a single blow; and all the people of
Hira applauded him. 'Antar then turned to the king and
finished his interrupted poem in such mellifluous style that the
verses have never been forgotten in Hira, and he ended thus:

' 'Antar kills the lion'

'So was the lion killed, and I turned to the king.

Though my sword is in my hand, still are my ankles
    fettered.

Yet perhaps in his mercy
    The king will free me.
Perhaps he will allow me to return to my love,
    And to my perfidious uncle,
Perhaps he will grant me the camels I so much desire.'

And King Mundhir was so delighted with 'Antar's courage
and with his verses that he promised him his liberty, and many
gifts (though not the camels, since these were the apple of his
eye) — for he recognized the sincerity of 'Antar's love and longing, and marvelled at his tenacity in facing up to a veritable
ocean of troubles and threats of destruction for the sake of an
Arab girl.

But before allowing 'Antar's departure (and, indeed, 'Antar
could not have left without the camels), King Mundhir
decided to enlist his help in establishing superiority over the
Persians since a rift had appeared in the king's relationship
with Chosroes, and where once there had been mutual respect
and admiration there was now bitter hatred and scorn. And
this is the story of the rift:

Mundhir was established by the Persian Emperor Chosroes
as Caliph of the Arabs, and Chosroes was a just ruler and a
man of good will. And every time that Mundhir visited the
Persian court he was received with honour and he dined at the
emperor's table and was given a rich robe. Now there was at
the court of Chosroes a certain chamberlain called Khosrowan, son of Jorhoum, lord of the Dailamites and comman-
der of more than twenty thousand Persian fighting men.
Khosrowan so hated Mundhir that there was no end to the lies
and treacheries he would employ against him, and he plotted
to bring about dissension between the emperor and the king in
the following manner. He said one day to the Emperor
Chosroes, 'O King of Kings, how can you continue to heap
your favours upon one of these idolatrous Arabs who are but
shepherds, and whose customs reveal only debauchery and
licence? These are men of no breeding, and you have no link
with such commoners. You will understand what I mean,' he
added, 'if, the next time you entertain the so-called King

Mundhir, you should offer him ordinary dates while serving stuffed dates to the rest of us. Watch him, then, and you will observe the coarse manners of this rustic ignoramus.' Thus, when the hour came for feasting on Mundhir's next visit, Chosroes made Mundhir sit beside him, and Mundhir did justice to the banquet spread before him. But when the dates were served, those given to Mundhir were whole dates while the rest of the company enjoyed dates stuffed with sugar and pistachio nuts in place of stones. And so Mundhir, seeing Chosroes and his courtiers eating the whole dates, tried to do likewise; the first he swallowed with difficulty, on the second he nearly broke a tooth, and at the third he choked. Then, flushed with wine and embarrassment, he looked up to see that all the courtiers were laughing. 'Why are your guests so merry?' he asked in confusion, and Chosroes said, 'O Mundhir, you are eating dates and swallowing the stones, and it is this which amuses us.' 'O King of Kings,' replied Mundhir, 'did I not do exactly as your own courtiers and as you did yourself?' 'Nay,' replied the emperor. 'Did you not perceive that we ate our dates so easily because the stones had been removed from them, and they had been filled with sugar?'

At this Mundhir's face darkened with anger, but he controlled his tongue out of respect for his emperor and, pitting his good manners against their ridicule, said only, 'O King of Kings, am I not your guest — have you invited me here only to mock me? Even so, I am your loyal servant and I thank you for the benefits bestowed upon me.' For, he thought to himself, it is because they differ in religion and customs that I must eat like them so as not to offend them in any way. But a few days later, in his own country and among his own men, Mundhir cried: 'O my countrymen, I have been grievously offended by the Emperor Chosroes and his chamberlain Khosrowan. Mount now and attack the Dailamites without mercy, for since the Day of the Dates I have sworn to avenge the outrage he has permitted, and to show that his name, once held in honour, is now derided among Arabs.' And it was at this meeting that 'Antar was brought a prisoner into his presence, and at which King Mundhir elicited 'Antar's help against his new enemy.

The Tenth Story

OF BATTLE AND TOURNAMENT

King Mundhir wrote to the Emperor Chosroes: 'You who know how to govern men, command that we be sent all those courtiers of yours who laughed at us, so that we may brand their faces with hot irons and show them the scorn of our tribesmen. Thus might we recapture the authority you would have us exercise over our tribesmen.' And Chosroes, in fury, dispatched Khosrowan to make Mundhir swallow his audacious words. And Khosrowan's army glowed in the sunshine like a river of silver beside the river of water, or like the waters of the great dam of Maarib bursting forth from the walls built to contain it so long ago. And Chosroes sent ahead his heralds to Mundhir, warning him to restrain his men; but Mundhir's men were already on the march and he said to Chosroes's heralds, 'What can I do, for I am a man of no authority?'

Now King Mundhir urged 'Antar to accompany him, but 'Antar was loath to do so for his heart yearned for 'Abla and he was desolate as an abandoned pasture; moreover, his horse Abjer had been wounded in the fighting when 'Antar stood alone against a thousand men. So Mundhir set out with his forces, and soon they saw in the distance the dust cloud which at once shields and betrays an army on the move. Khosrowan, riding upon a golden mare, was at the head of a great host, Persians and Dailamites, their silken banners gleaming in the sun and streaming in the wind. The desert throbbed to the sound of horses' hooves and the thud of marching feet, and over the jingle of harness rang the sound of trumpets and horns, and the whole host moved to the beating of their drums. The two armies clashed, and Mundhir's men gave way before the forces of the Persians, the Fireworshippers, and then fled towards Hira. Then 'Antar roused himself to help his host King Mundhir, remembering his clemency and gratitude to a helpless prisoner after the slaughter of the Khifan lion, and he borrowed a horse and rode into battle. King Mundhir swore by the Virgin and her Son (for he was a Christian) that if his army should after all triumph on the second day of battle, then would 'Antar receive even the camels he so much desired; and 'Antar swore by Lat and Uzza, gods of the sanctuary, that he would defeat the Fireworshippers. And this victory he accomplished on the following day, for he killed Khosrowan with his own hands, and swore that he would even place Mundhir upon the throne of Chosroes should this be his friend's desire.

But at this time, when the messengers were riding forth from the court of King Mundhir, summoning the tribes and all their allies to the fight, an ancient man rode out from the desert places and he was already four hundred years old. He sought out the Judge Mubidan, Qadi to Chosroes, and a man respected also by Mundhir, and together these two wise men worked for peace between the two factions. 'For,' said the ancient man, 'it is not written that the Fireworshippers should be enemies of these desert peoples in the west.' And he was believed, for he was a learned man who could follow the movement of the stars, and who had read all the books and all the stories in the world. And the ancient man was determined to make a peace between Chosroes and Mundhir.

Now it happened that the Governor of Antioch was accustomed every year to pay tribute to Chosroes, and while his presents were being packed, baled and loaded, they were seen by a traveller whose name is remembered as Badramout, or 'The Patrician'. He was of the Christian religion, and to him it seemed unworthy that a Christian governor of Antioch should send such tribute to Chosroes the Fireworshipper: precious metals and jewels, embroidered stuffs and vessels of gold and silver, and slave-girls, too, of great beauty. And the Patrician persuaded the governor to allow him to travel with this precious caravan to the east. 'And there,' he said, 'will I challenge these Fireworshippers to single combat, and since no one of them can vanquish me, then, by the True Cross, will I bring you back your treasure.' The Governor of Antioch agreed, although he warned the Patrician, 'Beware lest you open upon our kingdom a gate which you cannot close. And,' he added, prudently, 'should you be overpowered you must give the presents, and with good grace.' The Patrician agreed. He had confidence in his strength and in his God, and he thought nothing of the warning. He proceeded to the east over the desert after he had refreshed himself and strengthened his faith by visiting Holy Jerusalem and Siloam and the churches of Syria. And he met Chosroes's people and he challenged them, gambling for the treasure, and by the time the ancient man had approached Chosroes, the Patrician had fought in single combat for fourteen days, defeating all-comers. No one of his opponents had even scratched him. And Chosroes was extremely concerned that he might lose the tribute due to him from Antioch.

So, when the ancient man and Mubidan, the peacemakers, came to Chosroes and greeted him, and told him they could save him from this embarrassment, the Patrician, Chosroes was keenly interested. And the peacemakers said, 'O King of Kings, your battles with Mundhir will tear both your empire and his kingdom to pieces; but if you will do as we say and forget your quarrel, which is indeed of minor importance, being only an affair of dates, you may enjoy mutual peace as you enjoyed it before Khosrowan's jealousy brought about his death and your estrangement from Mundhir. Now the defeat of your army under Khosrowan,' they continued, 'was accomplished by 'Antar, son of Sheddad, a poet and a man of enormous strength and of unusual humility and virtue. If you will forget your quarrel with his friend King Mundhir,' they said, 'then will 'Antar, son of Sheddad, rid you of this upstart called the Patrician, for none can stand against him, though they have fought for fourteen days, but 'Antar can succeed.'

So Chosroes in his wisdom wrote a letter to Mundhir, and in it he made no mention of his defeated army nor of the dates, but simply asked Mundhir to come to the arena where the fighting between the Patrician and the Persian warriors was taking place; and to bring with him the noble knight 'Antar, son of Sheddad, of whom he had heard praises as a fighting man, as a virtuous man and as a poet. And Mundhir received the letter and was glad to send an answer in which he made no mention of his victorious army nor of the dates, for there was no doubt as to Chosroes's power, and King Mundhir had no desire to open upon his kingdom a gate he would be unable to close. But 'Antar sighed, for he feared this new adventure would delay him once again, and that it would yet be many weeks before he could escape the obligations of honour and meet again with his beloved 'Abla.

Chosroes meanwhile ordered a temporary halt to the great tournament, and instructed his magi to light a circle of fire and burn aloes from Comorin, invoking a victory for the Persian side; while the Christian monks who had accompanied the Patrician from the churches of Syria recited their gospels and crossed themselves, praying for a victory for their master.

And King Mundhir's men, with the king at their head, marched in peace towards Chosroes's country, to the place of the arena; and there to meet them was Chosroes himself in all his magnificence, his army arrayed as brave as peacocks. Mundhir was used to such sights, but 'Antar was astonished at the wealth and jewels displayed by Chosroes and his men. And the two leaders met as friends. But 'Antar marvelled, for Chosroes was dressed in a long robe of rosy silk embroidered with gold thread so that he resembled the rising sun, and his golden turban was decorated with pearls, and upon his fingers were diamonds and turquoises, beryls, onyx, sapphires and rubies, so that he dazzled the onlooker with each movement of his hands. And in his courtesy Chosroes suggested that if a fight were to be arranged between the Patrician and 'Antar, as was hoped, then this fight should await the dawn of the following day, giving 'Antar time to rest after his journey. But 'Antar cried, 'O King of Kings, your words are indeed full of wisdom and courtesy but I would wish to begin my combat with this Patrician as soon as I may'; and so it was arranged.

Now on the fourteenth day of the tournament the Patrician had been fighting with Bahram, a cousin of Khosrowan, so recently killed in battle. And Bahram was now ordered from the arena by Chosroes, and he was vexed, for he saw that he was to be replaced by none other than the slayer of his cousin; and he saw moreover that Chosroes admired 'Antar and that 'Antar already respected Chosroes. So Bahram watched from among the crowd, and his anger grew bitter within him, for it was soon apparent that 'Antar was a noble fighter. All day 'Antar battled with the Patrician, and once he even caught the Christian's lance, as it whistled towards him, in his strong and swarthy hand, and, turning it, flung it back towards the Patrician in one swift movement. As the crowd roared its approval of this brilliant manoeuvre, Bahram's rage overcame him and he said to himself, 'I will attack him from behind, and having killed him will also kill the Patrician in the confusion. Then will I have avenged my cousin, and all the honours of the kingdom will be heaped upon me for my valour.'

Bahram crept through the crowd unseen, and he aimed a terrible blow at 'Antar's back, but 'Antar, though intent upon the fight with the Patrician, had sensed the presence of a more treacherous enemy, and 'Antar turned and caught Bahram's javelin in his bare hand, and using it instead of his own great lance he hurled it at the Patrician and caught him full in the chest, so that the blade passed through his body and glittered crimson between his shoulder-blades, and the Patrician fell dead. And, as the crowd rose shouting to its feet, 'Antar crashed down upon the traitor Bahram with his lance, crying, 'O ignoble felon, now must you taste the reward of treachery.' And although Bahram fled he was caught by the hurtling lance and pinned to the dusty clods of the arena, where he died.

The magi and the monks departed from the arena, all dissatisfied with the outcome of their ceremonies and prayers; but the ancient man and Mubidan rejoiced that peace had been restored, at least between Chosroes and Mundhir; and as for 'Antar, he sighed to himself and said:

'Though I triumph, my heart is troubled.
In the land of the Hejaz are the tents of my own people,
    So far away.

Within those tents dwells my beloved,
    So far away.

Her hair is black, and she stands straight as a reed,
    But I am bowed down with troubles
And my adventures would have blanched white the hair
    Even of little children.

Yet after sorrow may come joy,
    For now I live in the country of a king,
Who is crowned by the sun, who cannot be hidden by
    the shadows.

All men have bodies, but he is all soul, unique in spirit,
    May he live for ever.'

This poem delighted Chosroes, and he honoured 'Antar
with a great banquet in his palace where the stools and tables
were made of ivory and ebony, the plates of silver and gold,
and where in the gardens cool fountains trickled beneath
cypress trees and the air was scented with violets as big as roses,
and roses as big as thornbushes. And Chosroes heaped upon
'Antar such presents as he had never dreamed of, and these
included the great triple tiara studded with gems and the
silken canopy embroidered with silver and gold, and its
emerald birds with topaz eyes, and many other gifts. 'Antar
drank the good wine, and ate, and enjoyed himself, and the
company laughed, but not in scorn, when he indicated his sur-
prise that they ate no camel's meat, the normal fare among the
tribes. Indeed, 'Antar learned that day to enjoy many new con-
fections. But he would not even watch the dancing girls,
murmuring to himself:

'Far from her whom he loves a man may only await her
    vision in his dreams,
Or a breeze may caress him, a breeze blowing from her
    country.
This very morning a breeze from the Hejaz brought me thy
    perfume and thy freshness, O my beloved.'

And he thanked Chosroes and left him marvelling at this
great and constant love. On the next day, 'Antar journeyed as
far as Hira with King Mundhir and Mundhir also showered
presents upon him, not forgetting the thousand flying camels
which have no wings but seem nevertheless to fly over the
desert on strong legs and velvet feet, making no more noise
than does an owl flitting across the silver sands by moonlight.
They were of all colours, from white to gold and from gold to
copper and so to black. Their trim bodies and humps were
rounded and full, and their woolly coats were soft as velvet,
and they moved to the sound of a thousand bells. And
Mundhir gave 'Antar also herdsmen and servants to look after
the caravan, and the two leaders bade farewell to each other,
Mundhir returning to Hira and 'Antar setting his face to the
west. And the herdsmen drove the camels before them, each

camel loaded with treasure as 'Antar had sworn they would be, and as they swung over the new-sprung grass and out on to the desert tracks, each with its long shadow, they resembled a great multi-coloured carpet thrown upon the land.

So at last 'Antar's task was completed, and he snuffed the desert wind, and from the wind he took his direction for home.

The Eleventh Story
RETURN AND THE FIRST ABDUCTION

When Shiboob through the kindness of an itinerant shepherd escaped from King Mundhir's men, he had watched and waited only until these men had driven off the hard-won camels, and then he started upon the long ride home, weeping for his brother 'Antar, whom he believed slain. And after many days he came to the Abs camp at sundown, and he could see the women of the tribe busy at their cooking pots and bread ovens, and the smoke from hundreds of fires rose in the still, cool air, for it was winter. But neither the cold air nor the burning camel-dung affected his eyes, for they were already sore with weeping. And all the tribe came out to meet this solitary horseman in the brief dusk before nightfall, and when night fell it was as though death itself had descended upon the camp, so grieved were all at this calamity. The lord Zuhair and his wife Temadhur wept for the hero of the tribe, and Sheddad, too, with Samiya his wife, and Zebeeba, mother of 'Antar, and Sheriya, mother of 'Abla, all wept; and as for 'Abla, her grief was such that she lay stunned and speechless as one fallen from a horse.

Yet did Amara the Coxcomb rejoice, anticipating his betrothal to 'Abla, and Rabia, too, was glad, for he hated 'Antar — but these two concealed their real feelings. And as for Amr, 'Abla's brother, he who considered 'Antar unworthy of his sister, and Malec, both men hid their contentment though secretly revelling in the success of the stratagem which seemed to have ended in 'Antar's death. But Shiboob told Zuhair of

84

Malec's treachery, and Malec and Amr were only allowed to continue dwelling in the tribe on sufference; and Rabia and Amara thought it politic to take their men away on a hunting expedition to last several weeks, so bitter was the feeling of the tribe which as yet but guessed at their perfidy.

The weeks passed, and the winter respite from the summer sun passed, and in the early spring, when the desert slopes are enamelled with tiny flowers and the tamarisks are washed and freshened by showers of sweet rain, two shepherd boys on the verge of the high desert saw a cloud of dust approaching, and one stayed to spy upon its cause while the other leapt upon the rump of his donkey, belabouring it with a stick; and he rode at speed to the camp, crying, 'We are attacked.' So the Prince and Sheddad and the other leaders went out to the desert's verge to defend the tribe, but the lord Zuhair remained to safeguard the camp itself.

And out of the dust there emerged a figure of enormous size, black and terrible, riding upon a black horse. And Shiboob cried out, 'O my lords, it is Abjer, and see, riding upon his back is my brother 'Antar preserved by the One God to return to us.' And Shiboob spurred his own horse towards 'Antar and the clouds of dust, and they met, and embraced. Then did all rejoice exceedingly at 'Antar's good fortune, and all was gaiety and excitement as the armed host mingled with 'Antar's great following, gasping in astonishment at the endless train of camels and horses and the loaded treasure and the herdsmen and slaves who accompanied their hero. And with the music of horns and pipes, and banners flying and drums beating, they rode into the camp where Zuhair, forewarned by a messenger, was preparing to greet them. 'Abla, all grief forgotten and all modesty abandoned, rode as upon wings to her beloved, crying, 'O 'Antar, son of my uncle, only with you can I find happiness. I had thought you dead, and I was left in darkness, but now you are with me and my sun has risen again' — and the two embraced in tears at their good fortune. And 'Abla rejoiced, and her mother also rejoiced; but Malec and Amr were enraged by 'Antar's unexpected return, and their looks and demeanour were sour and bitter as the taste of the Dead Sea apples which deceive the ignorant traveller in the desert with promise of sustenance and sweetness. And the two men, father and son, set off to seek Rabia and Amara and so avoid the celebrations of the tribe.

Now as 'Antar saw more of his friends advancing towards him and 'Abla, he became impatient to meet them, so he bade her farewell and left her in the care of her maidens and all those who had come so far to meet him; and he spurred Abjer to a gallop and sped across the space between, like an arrow shot by the Great Archer. For he was exultant. 'Even the whole earth,' he cried, 'cannot contain my love and my rejoicing!' And so he came to meet Zuhair and the remainder of his people.

But before long all the rejoicing was turned to grief and anxiety, for when those who had first met 'Antar came in from the far desert, 'Abla was not to be found among them. It was as though a jinn had spirited her away from the midst of the crowd. Yet later, O my listeners, the tale was told, and it happened thus:

'Abla found herself overcome by sleep in the noonday heat, and as her servants and she were passing the outlet of a small wadi where she knew there would be shade and water, she asked them to pause while she refreshed herself; and the servants did as they were bid, and before long all were sound asleep in the shade of the oleanders by the waterside.

Now this gave Amara a chance to realize his wicked intentions, for he had come out to meet 'Antar with both loathing and guile in his heart. Leading his horse silently over the soft sand, he came upon 'Abla in her slumber, and he leapt with her to the saddle and away without waking her companions. And the flying camels passed in endless train by the opening of the wadi so that all 'Abla's cries were lost in the jingle of a thousand bells, and not even the tracks towards the tiny spring and away to the east were found until a day had passed.

'Abla soon ceased from her screaming and savaged Amara with her tongue, but could do little against his strength. So it was that the horse with its double burden headed for Yemen, unheard and unperceived.

Now Amara intended riding till he came to the country of Meljem ibn Handala, but before long he was surrounded by a party of three hundred horsemen led by Mufarraj ibn Hamam, and he could go no further. But so bitter was the quarrelling between 'Abla and Amara that, dismounted, they scorned and savaged each other despite their predicament, almost ignoring their captors. And, watching there, Mufarraj ibn Hamam came to admire 'Abla's spirit and her ready wit, sharpened by anger as it was; and he desired her for himself. So both the fugitives were taken, and when they came to the camp of Mufarraj he handed them over to the servants of his venerable aunt, saying to her, 'See now, O sister of my mother, these two quarrelsome Absians have been captured by my men in the far desert. The young coxcomb I will keep as a hostage against many camels, for I doubt not that he is of noble blood, so rare are the garments he wears. The damsel I would preserve for myself. She is as courageous as she is beautiful and I hope to win her heart.' And on the following day he approached her, but she turned upon him like a scorpion disturbed, and he made no progress. Then Mufarraj became angry with the pair of them, and for many days he caused Amara to be beaten thrice, and 'Abla once, between sunrise and sunset — though in truth it did little to advance his cause. Finally Selma, his aunt, became weary of Amara's curses and lamentations and of 'Abla's cries, and persuaded her nephew to allow 'Abla to become her own servant, and thus 'Abla was set to do many menial tasks, among them the milking of the buffaloes. 'Abla would press her lovely face against their velvet flanks, and she would weep as she worked, dreaming of 'Antar: and the great beasts seemed to join in her melancholy, their huge eyes filling with tears which dripped sadly from their long, dark lashes.

But meanwhile 'Antar and Shiboob and many others had set off to try to rescue 'Abla, and it was borne in upon them that Amara must be the culprit; and indeed, after some days, a message arrived for Rabia, conveyed by a band of gipsies with whom Amara had managed to converse briefly and in secret. And Rabia was overcome with anger and disgrace at confirmation of the actions of his brother, and he cried, 'Shame upon him who so maltreats a girl of his own tribe!' He sent the gipsies on their way and told nothing of the affair to Zuhair, knowing that the lord would have said to him, 'You have schemed continually against 'Antar, O my cousin, and have demanded his blood. And now your own brother has stolen 'Antar's betrothed in a manner unworthy of an Arab warrior.' So Rabia and his friend Urwa took their men and set out secretly upon the way the gipsies had directed them.

Shiboob and 'Antar had by this time advanced far along the stony track to Yemen, and had camped at the spot where 'Abla and Amara had clearly been overpowered; and Shiboob advanced further by night, and alone, and in the darkness he came upon Mufarraj's camp, and he heard 'Abla weeping in the little tent set up for her near the tethered buffaloes. He heard her song of love and longing, and her lamenting, and he slipped away to his master; but first he whispered to 'Abla that help was on the way. And on Shiboob's return 'Antar fainted for very joy at the news that his beloved had been found. Later he sent for the Prince and Malec and Sheddad, and for Zuhair, who came muttering, 'May God Himself curse the family of Zaiyad.' And when all were prepared they advanced together.

At this time Mufarraj sent messengers to the Absians demanding ransom for Amara, and while waiting for their return he pestered 'Abla with his advances, but she would have none of him and prayed he might not become too earnest to be held at bay by words, for she had no better weapon. And Amara suffered as badly as she, for Selma discovered that he had in fact killed her own son in a raid not long before, though the name of her son's murderer been unknown to her, and now she sought revenge. So every day she would have him beaten, and moreover would tease and bite him, and confuse him with alternate messages from Mufarraj which brought sometimes hope and sometimes despair, until Amara cracked before her and was as helpless as an owl in daylight, at his wits' end. And he would spend his days groaning and repenting his past sins.

Then came Anis the Misogynist, a messenger from Rabia, seeking to trick Mufarraj and his men into advancing from the camp. 'For,' he said, 'although the Absians are near, they are a party of only ten men.' But though Mufarraj would have fallen into this snare, yet was Selma cleverer than her nephew, and her scouts reported that there were not ten but two hundred horsemen near by. So Anis was seized and bound and imprisoned with Amara as the untrustworthy messenger that he was. And Anis reproached Amara bitterly for his disgraceful folly.

But the forces were gathering against Mufarraj, and so it came about that a tremendous battle was fought between him and the troops of Rabia, and those of Zuhair, and those of 'Antar: and men recount to this very day how Mufarraj captured Qais, brother of the Prince and Shas, and how many were killed on both sides, and how Rabia was out-manoeuvred. For he and his men were separated from their waterskins and became enfeebled in the heat of the day, and were indeed upon the point of death. 'Yet would we die in battle rather than surrender,' cried Rabia, who for all his wickedness was a noble warrior. 'Send, then, an equal number of your men to attack us so we may perish under our own standards, fighting to the end.'

One of Rabia's men, Jamil the Orator, so humbled himself as to beg for water for his fellows, and it appeared that Mufarraj softened until, having captured Jamil, he laughed and offered to protect him on account of his oratory; and Mufarraj ignored Jamil's fellow-men. And all were appalled at Mufarraj's contemptible behaviour. Yet the very scandal of it spurred those who fought against him to rally again to their leader, Rabia, and they beat off all attacks until nightfall when they were able, in the darkness, to reach some of their waterskins and share the dwindling supply of water, and rest and tend their wounds.

'Abla was half-pleased to see the discomfiture of the Zaiyad, who had caused her so much suffering, yet was she endangered, for at nightfall Mufarraj sat drinking till he was flushed with wine, and he desired 'Abla and sent Selma to fetch her. And 'Abla cursed Selma and she cursed Mufarraj, but she was dragged nevertheless from her tent and her screams warned the other prisoners of her impending fate and they thought to themselves, If she does not submit we shall surely die; and Urwa thought, Truly this damsel has brought ill-fortune upon us all — for like many wrongdoers, he could not see his own blame in the matter, but only that of others.

Yet Mufarraj was not to have his desires fulfilled, for 'Antar and the Prince crept up to the camp in the darkness, and as the moon rose they fell upon the defenders. 'Abla then watched while Mufarraj armed himself uncertainly in the semi-darkness of his tent where she had been dragged unwillingly. Yet was the wine too much for him, his courage deserted him and he fled. But Selma seized a sword and a horse and spurred her steed against the attackers, till she was disarmed and allowed to follow her worthless nephew in his headlong flight. So, when dawn broke rosy and warm over the desert, the lovers were once again united; and 'Antar washed from his body the blood which had covered him like a crimson robe, and he sang of the battle:

'O 'Abla, since night, and a pall of dark dust, shrouded my
    deeds from you in the combat,
Ask my horse! Ask him! Did I slacken against an enemy
    numerous as the stars?

Ask my lance, did it not thrust well between the turban
    and the beard?
Ask my sword, did it not sever the heads of noble leaders
    in this battle?

I quenched the thirst of my sword and the thirst of my
    spear.
I have been fearless fighting fearless men for thy favour.

The All-Powerful has built up the firmament.
Now in my triumph I could ride among the stars,
Astride the black night, as though this were my charger.'

And 'Abla rode home in safety with her lover, mounted
upon Abjer, and with the words of 'Antar's poem burning in
her heart.

The Twelfth Story

THE WOMAN OF KINDA

Now it happened, O my listeners, that 'Abla's health suffered from the beatings she had received at the hands of Selma, the fearsome aunt of Mufarraj ibn Hamam. And during the fighting 'Antar became fully aware of the perfidy of Rabia and of Amara and of Malec and of his cousin Amr, and he complained bitterly to Malec, saying, 'O my uncle, how can I depend upon your word of honour as an Arab, for when your daughter, my beloved, is in danger, do you not promise me her hand in marriage, yet when she is safe I become in your eyes nothing but a slave. Moreover, such is the discord in the tribe as a result of your irresolute behaviour, that others more vicious than yourself have intervened, and now I hear that Rabia, to whom 'Abla has been entrusted in the perils of battle, desires protection for her from my uncle Shas; whereas Malik the Prince would protect her better from the wrangling and plotting of her own people.'

Now all were astonished to hear 'Antar speak so furiously to the elder men, and there was much whispering among them as they sought to reply to his anger. But 'Antar turned upon them, crying, 'Nay, I will listen neither to your excuses nor to your further scheming. Let 'Abla stay with her mother, and let her be under the protection of the Prince. I call on you all to witness. My soul is sick of treachery and I shall leave you all to seek for spiritual refreshment.' So he left, walking alone with Shiboob, the two men leading Abjer and the other horses on a halter's end, for like their masters these noble animals were

91

scarred and tired in conflict. Yet 'Antar paused at the desert's edge and called to his tribe, in a voice of new authority, 'Remember, O my uncles, should there be even the whisper of any betrothal arranged for my fair cousin I will assuredly hear of it, for the very birds of the desert are my friends, and I swear before the one God of Abraham, the Friend of God, that I will slaughter any man who dares raise his miserable eyes towards 'Abla, be it Chosroes himself, or the Emperor of Rome beyond the greater sea.' So he moved on towards the darkening east, with his brother and the horses; and the men of Abs were left dismayed and melancholy as the night fell upon them all.

'Antar and Shiboob travelled quietly, seeking the groves of Mecca where, even before the days of the Prophet, upon whom be peace, was already a sanctuary. And here no blood could ever be shed, and even criminals could find shelter; and here in Mecca men looked for purification and for time to reflect on mysteries as yet not totally revealed to the desert peoples. Now, as they travelled, the burden of man's wickedness became less heavy to 'Antar and his brother, and they pondered on the will of the gods. And 'Antar, as he rode (for Abjer was now strong enough to bear him), mused in poetry upon his love for 'Abla, and with melancholy — for his was a life of hope deferred, and this, as the wise Jews have it in their proverbs, maketh the heart of a man sick within him.

On the fourth day of their journey, health and good cheer began to return to the brothers, and the horses went more lively; when all at once they heard a cry, and turning from their path to a tiny oasis they found a woman, with her husband lying wounded by her side in the shade of the tamarisk bushes and a few palm sprigs, and with them was their daughter, newly widowed and weeping by the well's side.

They were of the Kinda people, and the woman begged help for her husband, Ashath ibn Obad, gravely wounded in the ambush; and for her daughter, whose husband had died in her defence. The woman mourned her three sons who had died with him, and she cursed the warrior, Sudam ibn Salheb, and his followers, crying, 'May all the ghouls of hell descend upon him in their wrath.' And 'Antar rallied to her help, pursuing Sudam; and 'Antar slaughtered the bandits one by one till Sudam alone was left. Then cried Sudam, 'We are men, you and I. Let us not fight, but band together and live well on those travellers who head for the Sacred Valley, their minds on things other than their own defence.' But 'Antar would have none of it, and he killed Sudam. Then he returned to the well's side, and helped the woman and her daughter to prepare a litter for Ashath, and to transport him to the nearest camp. And he left with them horses and booty taken from the murderers, so that their safety was assured. And the woman of Kinda praised 'Antar in a poem of great merit, saying:

'Now we have seen his firmness,
His strength in our protection,
His selfless spending of his strength in our protection.

Here is a noble Arab,
A true friend to the weak and the suffering.'

And 'Antar, deeply moved, answered her with verses of his own, which were later to be the saving of his uncle's life, for he cried,

'Had I not aided you, my mother,
Had I not spent my strength in your protection,
Cursed would I have wandered over the rough sands —
Cursed as one who honoureth not womankind.'

And he and Shiboob continued upon their way, greatly cheered by the accomplishment of this kindness.

Sheddad, meanwhile, approached Zuhair in anger over the broken promises made to his son: and Malec countered him, crying, 'It is Shas's decision that my daughter marry Amara. I objected, indeed, remembering the wealth 'Antar had offered her; but, "Folly," Shas said, and, "I will make terms with 'Antar," Shas said, and since 'Antar has gone from among us, does not this prove that I am right?' Yet did Zuhair silence him with a glance of contempt, and to Sheddad he said, 'We will await Shas's return, and when all are assembled we will draw some sensible outcome from this confusion, and from the immorality which has so disgusted 'Antar that he has sought solitude and comfort in the Sacred Groves.' So they waited, but dawn broke and yet another dawn, and still Shas did not come.

And after three days, the lord Zuhair arose and said, 'Alas for us all, has this base conduct brought misery upon Shas, as it has upon 'Antar? I am in a fair mind to kill not only Amara but Malec also because of their cunning and their lies, and their malevolence.' Yet he stayed his hand throughout a further day, and still there was no sign of Shas or his huntsmen.

And here, O my listeners, is the story of Shas. He rode fast and far in pursuit of deer and game; and he was separated from his men, and captured by Maisur ibn Zaiyad of the Hazrej. And since Shas had been responsible for the death of Shiban, Maisur's brother, Maisur took him off to the lands around Hareth there to torture him. But Shas aroused the pity of Maisur's wife and her companions, and one day, in the absence of the menfolk, she let him plead for his release; and he stayed with the women under the shade of the tamarisks all the warm afternoon, brewing coffee and exchanging stories.

There was one woman, a stranger, who suggested that they should recite poetry, and she began with some lines, already famous, about the Holy Valley. Whereupon Shas, his bonds and discomfiture half-forgotten, capped them with a verse of 'Antar's on the same subject. And so vivid was this poem that 'Antar's true self shone forth from the very words. And Shas ended with a simple verse on the beauty of the tamarisks under which they were sitting, extolling their rosy flowers and their magic quality of attracting the silver dew of a desert dawn to their own spare branches. Then the stranger recognized the poem, for she was the woman of Kinda, and she told all the company of 'Antar's nobility and kindness.

Shas then repented of his wrongdoing towards 'Antar, whom he had blamed for worldly lusts and whose chivalry he had ignored. And he begged the woman to help him, and she helped him, dressing him in woman's clothing and darkening his face and hands with a black stain so that he escaped, unrecognized in the darkness, on a stolen horse. So Shas was freed, and as he headed for home he was overtaken by two horsemen whom he scarcely dared to face — 'Antar himself, and Shiboob, returning, refreshed, from Mecca. And Shas wept, begging forgiveness.

Then said 'Antar, 'O Shas, grieve not for the past,' and he comforted his uncle with true kindness, and again warned Shiboob, who was still very angry, to renounce ill will, 'For,' he said, 'no one can act justly when actuated by ill will.' So in new harmony the three set off for home, and Shas stopped only to wash the stain from his hands and his face, and to change into a man's clothing.

Thus it happened that, some days later, Shiboob rode ahead to tell the tribe of their approach, and all came out to welcome those who had been lost. A bitter silence reigned among the family of Zaiyad, who knew not where to look, but to all the rest it was a glad meeting, and a feast was prepared, and wine flowed for three days. Then, on the fourth day, Shas took over the celebrations and supported the betrothal of 'Antar to 'Abla, nor would he welcome Malec at the rejoicings. And Shas, in genuine remorse, offered 'Antar all his possessions. But 'Antar refused, saying, 'Good feeling between you and me is great enough reward for any service I have done you, O my uncle.' And 'Antar visited 'Abla in her mother's tent; but Amara, sick with disappointment, took to his bed, and remained there for many days.

The Thirteenth Story

'ABLA'S UNREASONABLE
DEMANDS

While 'Antar was away, O my listeners, the men
and women, and above all the children of the tribe, had not
enjoyed 'Abla's lovely presence among them, nor heard her
merry laughter, for she lay sick as a result of her former
captivity and because of her anxiety for 'Antar in his long
absence. But it seemed to her friends that, with 'Antar's
return, and with the rescue of Shas, her uncle, and Shas's
support for the betrothal, the stars of fortune might again
shine upon 'Abla and she might once more enchant them with
her smile. Yet two things happened at this time which were to
delay her happiness, and this is the first of them.

'Abla emerged from her tent after the great feast Shas made
for his protector 'Antar; she seemed stronger, but yet still cast
down — for had not 'Antar declared he must go in battle
against the Qahtan once more before their marriage? This
delay cut 'Abla to the heart, though she spoke no word of it,
and she lay upon a litter in the shade of the tamarisks, her
maidens and her friends around her, trying to bring a smile to
her pale face. And one day it was observed that her uncle,
Rabia, came thus to speak with her as she rested in the shade.
All one long afternoon he spoke with her until the shadows
lengthened and the yellow evening light caught the smoke
from the dung fires and turned it to a mist of gold. And her
friends thought, How good he is to try to entertain her. Yet
Rabia was bent upon a furtive and perfidious design, for he
saw that 'Abla's spirit had suffered, and that the seeds of

unreason which he could implant in her mind might well develop into some strangling vine which could overthrow 'Antar as creepers may envelop and destroy the sweet-scented bead tree* whose leaves protect us from winged insects in the warmth after the winter rains.

Malec now instructed 'Abla to prepare for her marriage, yet in his meanness he disputed with 'Antar about the marriage feast, and indeed 'Abla knew well that her father favoured Amara rather than 'Antar as his prospective son-in-law, and she was doubly distressed and confused. While 'Antar, unable fully to understand her disappointment at his new departure, indulged himself too freely in his uncle's wine. So that when he and Malec came to speak with 'Abla next morning, Rabia's poison had worked well, and 'Abla astounded both the men by demanding, in a most unreasonable manner, a wedding feast comparable to that of Jaida bint Zahir when she married her cousin Khaled ibn Moharib. 'Antar was ignorant of the story, but Malec was appalled at his daughter's knowledge, and foresaw endless troubles arising from her request, which he could only believe arose from the fevers of a troubled mind.

And here, O my listeners, is the story of Khaled and Jaida:

There were once two brothers, and love was strong between them. But they quarrelled. And as is the way with mankind, hatred replaced the love between them, and seemed seven times the stronger. One was Moharib, chief of his tribe; the other, Zahir, his trusted adviser.

After the quarrel Zahir and his wife Asma' could find no pleasure among their former companions, and so they left to seek shelter with the Sa'ad people. And eight months later Asma' became the mother of a daughter, Jaida. And Na'ila, the wife of Moharib, at about the same time became the mother of a son, Khaled. But Asma' and Zahir, fearing Moharib's scorn and triumph, pretended from the first that Jaida was in fact a boy, so they named her Joodr and educated her as if she were their son.

Jaida learned the martial arts and became skilled in horsemanship and the use of arms; and the fame of her exploits spread throughout the tribes until it reached the ears of her cousin, Khaled. Jaida revelled in her accomplishments, for so far nothing had occurred to reveal to her any of the joys of

*This tree is Persian lilac, *Melia azedarach*.

97

womanhood, and she thought of herself as one of a long line of Arab girls who had triumphed on equal terms with Arab men. 'I am destined,' she said to herself, 'to be another Robab, or a new Zenobia, she who led her father's men into battle and defeated even the Romans in the old days when Palmyra was still a proud city at the height of its beauty.'

Now at this time Moharib abu Khaled died, and Khaled, remembering the renowned exploits of his cousin Joodr, took with him a small party of horsemen and rode through the deserts to visit his uncle Zahir; and in Khaled's heart were two aims, the one to repair the rifts within his tribe, the other to challenge his cousin Joodr in combat.

But Zahir and Asma' had come to hear of Moharib's death, and they saw now no reason to continue with the deception in which they had involved their daughter, and regardless of Jaida's protest and Khaled's puzzlement, the two young people met as woman and as man, and now at last was Jaida discomfited and rebuffed, for at the very sight of her handsome cousin she lost her martial heart to him, and her woman's instincts overwhelmed her utterly, as the floods of autumn sweep through the steep canyons of Petra, carrying all before them. So she stood baffled and dismayed before Khaled. The young man was both puzzled and embarrassed by his silent cousin and, untouched by love, he could not but reveal his disappointment as to her sex.

Now it is the habit of mothers the world over to plot and plan for the happiness of their children, even against their children's wishes, and so it came about that Asma' and Na'ila, who had been dear friends before their husbands' quarrel, came together to ponder on these strange events, and Jaida confided her new feelings to her mother's keeping, and her mother, with Na'ila's help, lost no time in telling Khaled the true position: that he had won his cousin's heart. Khaled could take no joy in this, and indeed he left hurriedly with his men for the desert, saying to his mother, 'I am as yet too young for marriage, and I do not believe there is a girl who could touch my heart. Moreover,' he added, 'your choice and the choice of my Aunt Asma' can never be my own choice . . . ' And he added more, which he afterwards repented, and he left his mother and his aunt and poor Jaida in a state of dejection and dismay.

But Jaida's pride came to her rescue, and she rallied, and defied her parents, saying, 'O my parents, can you not see that it is impossible for me to change almost overnight from boy to girl, from man to woman — I am confused by these events and must be off into the desert on a hunting trip and maybe this will restore the balance of my mind.' So she, too, left for the desert.

Now Khaled was determined to challenge the young men of the Sa'adi tribe, and he arranged a tournament in the wilderness, yet not too far from their main camp; and Khaled was more skilful than all comers, so that on the third day he had defeated every adversary. But as the combatants and the watching crowds were thinking of dispersing, there rode into their midst a horseman whom all could recognize by his dress and habit as a Hejazi. Then did Khaled challenge the Hejazi, who was none other than Jaida in disguise, and they fought from noon until sundown and neither one could unhorse or even scratch the other; for, as with Robab and Jazima, Jaida's horsemanship was so superb that Khaled's superior strength was unavailing. For three days they fought, but neither one could gain the advantage.

Then on the fourth day Khaled saw his opponent mount for a further contest, and his curiosity overcame him, and with sword lowered he cried, 'Peace, stranger, let us put an end to this stalemate. Maybe the gods would see us friends rather than enemies.' And at this the Hejazi drew the kefiyeh from his face and revealed the face of Jaida, flushing in the morning light with triumph and merriment. 'Nay, cousin,' she cried, turning her horse, 'when I would have proffered friendship, and indeed more than friendship, you would not accept it!' And with a smile more dazzling than the sunlight reflected on the sweet waters of Maarib, she spurred her steed and galloped off into the far desert at such speed that none were of a mind to follow.

Thus was Khaled abashed before his friends, and more so because at the instant of Jaida's smiling his heart was lost into her keeping, and he felt such passion for his cousin that all other interests faded before its heat. And he swallowed his pride and consulted with his mother, first having begged her pardon for his unfilial harshness. 'For,' he said to her, 'is not the arranging of marriages a woman's joy?' But Jaida's pride would not permit her to comply with Khaled's evident wishes, though she was amazed at her own temerity.

And now although the tribes and the families favoured a

marriage, Jaida would not consent; and to win time she **made** unreasonable demands of her lover, insisting upon conditions such as the capture of a thousand camels, property of the Spear-Thrower, and upon a noble woman, free born, to hold her camel's bridle. But Khaled won for her all that she demanded. So — half-wavering — she rode out with him in the desert, teasing and tormenting him until he cried, 'Nay, cousin, let us bring an end to our conflict. Let us part if we may not wed.'

But now there emerged from the rocks two lions, huge and dreadful in aspect, their manes red as the dust from the Jebel Hamrin which, borne upon the wind, may colour the hot skies of all 'Iraq with a rusty cloud. And Jaida and Khaled banded together in their own defence, and they fought and killed the lions; and in so doing they came to see that a great love bound them together. Khaled then found courage to approach his intimidating bride with a proper manliness, and he embraced her; and she was not insensible to the delights of a surrender which had hitherto seemed unthinkable. So they married, and during the celebrations Jaida's camel was led by a noble woman, free born.

But yet was Jaida to pay heavily for her pride.

So also would 'Abla pay for the unreasonable conditions which Rabia had furtively induced her to demand. 'Antar abandoned his challenge to the Qahtan and left with Shiboob to fulfil the requests, aiming at the capture of Jaida herself, and proposing to force this free-born woman to lead 'Abla's camel at the wedding feast.

And it came about that the gods punished both Jaida and 'Abla for their unreason. In Khaled's absence, Jaida was guarding their territory with a party of but twenty rangers, alert and watchful. Yet they were surprised by 'Antar and Shiboob, and were overwhelmed though the two brothers had difficulty in subduing the elusive Jaida and her quicksilver mare. She was wounded and taken captive indeed, but yet escaped by a ruse, and she fled to join her husband. And the whole tribe prepared for battle. So was Zubaid set against the Abs raiders.

Now in the Abs camp chaos and confusion had arisen over 'Antar's departure, and Zebeeba, mother of 'Antar, was sent for by Sheddad, his father, to find out what had occurred; and 'Abla — for the first time in her life — trembled before the wrath of Zebeeba, and before the anger of Sheddad, and before the fury of her uncle Shas, for, as the illness drained from her body and from her mind, she saw her own unworthiness and recognized the criminal stupidity which her devious uncle Rabia had so skilfully encouraged to develop in her brain. And she wept before them in shame and self-contempt, with all her courage spent; for who can face up to fate when he is unsure of his own real virtue? So we must leave her weeping and dejected, and, indeed, racked with anguish, as she pictured all that might follow from her folly.

But the men of the tribe, not without enjoyment, prepared for battle, and they drummed out of the camp on horseback, led by Zuhair himself, and the lord called out: 'Courage, men, for I shall raise our standards at Nika.' Then, as darkness fell, the dust settled behind Zuhair's warrior host.

To Shas fell the guarding of the women and the flocks, and, disappointed, he turned upon Malec, who pretended anger with his foolish daughter, but in reality hoped that Rabia's plot would end in 'Antar's destruction. Yet Shas knew his cousin too well to believe him, and he rent him with his tongue, which was indeed no mean weapon, and in his fury he set upon Malec with a whip; and Malec cringed, crying, 'Alas, I am ignoble and have betrayed my tribe and my daughter, and you my cousin Shas, and I have no future here among you. I will rid you all of my unwelcome presence, I shall fly to the Syrian hills and there join with those who worship the Cross!' And so he moaned and shrank before Shas until Rabia, and others among the Zaiyad, feeling themselves tainted by his shame and insulted by Shas's behaviour, left the camp, a party of some eight hundred souls, carrying 'Abla with them.

And Rabia said, 'Let us follow 'Antar's tracks. He may well be killed by Jaida and Khaled and their men. We will camp by the nearest well, and in the event of his death, and the battle between Khaled and Zuhair which must assuredly follow, Zuhair will have need of us and may forgive our past iniquities.' So they camped at the Khirjein wells. And they were captured there by Khaled's men, and once again was 'Abla a prisoner. Indeed, in her grief and anxiety she felt some relief at this, for ever in her mind, when she was in Zaiyad company, was the fear of a forced marriage with the foppish Amara. But her relief was swallowed up in anguish when the main attack was launched by 'Antar and Shiboob, and by the lord Zuhair;

and 'Abla was forced to watch the slaughter of Khaled, a brave and noble man. Many other noble men, and many horses, lay dead upon the sand that day, and the sight was to haunt 'Abla for years to come, for had it not been her pride which caused such pointless turmoil? Furthermore, even had she wished for it, which she now did not, there was no noble and free-born hostage among the women to lead her camel on the day of her marriage, for Jaida, elusive as ever, was once more rescued by her men, and fled, wounded and grief-stricken but free, into the far desert to recoup her forces.

So all that remained to 'Abla was remorse, just as all that remains of the watchman's fire of living thorns are the grey ashes and a few black stones. But the Abs forgave her lapse into unreason, reserving their wrath for the Zaiyad, whose movements and motives were suspect, despite Rabia's excuses. 'In our hearts,' he said, 'we sought only the safety of our noble nephew 'Antar, and to help him and the lord Zuhair we camped where we camped. I ask you, O my friends,' he cried, 'what other reasons could we have had for waiting there?'

And although many could have answered him, there was, in this instance, no reply.

The Fourteenth Story

THE TWO SLAVES AND 'ABLA'S TREASURE

Later the two unlucky lovers were again separated by the evil-doing of Malec, who, held in contempt by many in the tribe, left camp, taking 'Abla with him. 'Antar and his companions moved in to Fazara country, following others of the tribe. Everything seemed to conspire in tormenting his longing. It was spring. The desert was abloom with tiny flowers, the turtle doves were flighting. 'Antar, alone, fed upon his sorrow without even Shiboob to cheer him, for he had disappeared.

But the faithful Shiboob had set himself the task of watching over 'Abla, and he discovered her and her father to be guests of the Shaban tribe, led by Qais ibn Masud. And Shiboob discovered also that Malec, evilly advised by Rabia, had determined once more to bring about 'Antar's death. He promised 'Abla to Bustam, son of Qais, and for a brideprice demanded 'Antar's head, just as the venomous Salome, so long ago, enticed from Herod, king of the wise Jews, the head of Hanna, forerunner to the Prophet Issa.

And Bustam set out to find 'Antar, resolving not to come back empty-handed. Yet Shiboob, with his desert craft, outstripped him, and he warned his brother. New life flooded back into 'Antar's veins as he learned of 'Abla's plight, and he and Shiboob rode off together at speed, both refreshed and outraged by the turn of events.

The rivals met and fought together for two days, and over the desert came men from the Abs and men from the Shaban tribes, and a general battle developed in which finally 'Antar was victorious, and Bustam found himself alone among a hundred and one enemies, and he laid down his sword.

Now, in Bustam's absence, his own people had been attacked and overwhelmed by the Temim, and so were the captors captive; and with them 'Abla and her father and her brother. And the Temim moreover had taken Badur, the beautiful one, favourite sister of Bustam. And when he heard this Bustam wept, and he offered his services to 'Antar if he would but rescue not only 'Abla but also Badur from the new perils surrounding them. 'Antar and the Abs were moved by his distress, and battle was sought and won against the Temin, with Abs and Shaban fighting side by side. But Malec had by now sunk so low that he was in danger of forgetting the noblest of Arab virtues, loyalty to his tribe and its leaders; and once more he left in silence, and by night, accompanied by his lovely and long-suffering daughter 'Abla. For in those days, O my listeners, the word of a father was law.

Now Malec and his men came to Kinda lands, and were guests of the sheikh Amr; and Malec held Mashil, Amr's nephew, spellbound with stories of 'Abla's talents, so that Mashil amassed great wealth as a price for a bride whom he contrived to see by the ruse of disguising himself as a girl. Cattle there were, and camels; satin robes and silks, and jewels, and balls of dark musk; and slaves, and among these Rabiat, a girl of many gifts.

But 'Antar, with Bustam and the Prince, who was a guide to the younger men as is the North Star to those who track up from the Great Barrier to the Great River where the date palms flourish, moved against Kinda. And they were possessed not only of victory, but also of the cattle and camels, the satin robes and the silks, the precious jewels and the balls of dark musk which Mashil had assembled; and instead of the delights of love, Mashil faced the final terror of death, and many of his men died with him.

Then 'Abla regained the Abs camp, and she was happy to be placed under the protection of the Prince rather than that of her father, 'For,' she said, 'the Prince's mind is superior to all others, and he shows courtesy to all.' The treasure was put under 'Antar's care, and Malec hid his face in shame, venturing from his tent only to plot with his son Amr, and with Rabia and Amara.

Now 'Abla was delighted with the company of her new servant Rabiat, and the two girls became great friends, and

Rabiat would tell 'Abla of her life before she became a prisoner of the Kinda peoples, and of her love for Bashara, another slave among these people. And 'Abla herself, at that time so accustomed to unfulfilled love, would listen to the tale of Rabiat's sorrows and vow to help her. And indeed her kindness of heart brought its reward, for Rabia's plots came to fruition and 'Abla was enticed to the desert pools one moonlit night, with her maid Rabiat, and 'Abla was captured by a party of ten horsemen, and many of her jewels and treasures were seized with her, for Rabia had tricked the girls into bringing them to this dark assignation, hinting that he needed them for some barter dealing of her father's. So 'Abla was seized by men who had been told she was an adulteress whose crimes deserved death. 'But the execution,' Rabia had whispered to these fanatics, 'must not take place on our territory, lest perchance her evil spirit should haunt the waters of our own oasis.'

Rabiat, her heart bursting with rage and pity, was left bound with cords upon the water's edge, until, towards dawn, she freed her ankles from their bonds, and stumbled back to the camp as the sun rose.

Grief and anger roused all the tribe, and as they marshalled their forces, Rabia slipped from the camp to meet his hired go-between, Mufarraj, and they came to the appointed place where the horsemen were to assemble; and they heard, as they approached, the high, musical voice of 'Abla disputing earnestly with Sinan, leader of the fanatics. 'Nay, sir,' she was crying, facing him in assurance of her virtue, 'you are mistaken, I am no adulteress, and you and your men should be ashamed to accuse me, for you have no knowledge of me or my noble tribe, and indeed are strangers to us all. Moreover,' she continued, fervent in defence of the right, and fearless as Robab, 'I am to be released immediately and set upon my way, and I can pay a good price for one of your horses since my uncle, who arranged this infamous abduction, tricked me into bringing my jewels with me, even as he tricked you into leaving your good sense behind you.'

The men muttered uneasily at this unexpected defiance, and Sinan was aghast to hear her story, for he believed her every word, and he and his men were fanatical for the truth. So when Rabia appeared with Mufarraj, Sinan turned angrily upon them both, saying, without greeting, 'O deceivers, neither I nor my men will take any further part in this plot.'

And they fled, taking with them only one ring for their part in the adventure, for fanatics are sometimes simple-hearted, and can be touched by beauty as well as by virtue, and 'Abla's loveliness and courage had moved them all.

Now Rabia vowed to himself that he and Mufarraj together must be responsible for 'Abla's death, which would appease Amara's jealous anguish and avenge the Zaiyad against the black upstart 'Antar, whom they hated. So they seized 'Abla, and she rode on Mufarraj's saddlebow before him, yet was she unsure as to the identity of her two captors, since both were muffled about the face and silent. And they rode in silence till they reached a small camp wherefrom they stole two horses, and they forced a slave into accompanying them into the quiet of the desert beyond the earshot of men and dogs alike.

Now this slave was none other than Bashara, lover of Rabiat; and he had fled from Kinda in the fighting and was sheltering in his mother's tent.

Then the two would-be murderers handed 'Abla over to the slave, together with a dagger of fine workmanship, its handle bound with silver cord and set with precious gems, and they cried, 'Away, O slave, and kill this girl who is a menace to us all, and if you accomplish your task, you may keep the dagger as a reward, but should you fail us, then we shall see that you are returned to the master you have left, and he will punish you for your flight. And do not seek to evade us, for our horses are fleeter than the two nags upon which you and 'Abla are mounted.' And they wheeled and galloped off in a cloud of dust, leaving 'Abla and Bashara face to face as the dust and the quiet of the desert settled around them.

Now Shiboob had already set off upon the trail of the ten horsemen to search for 'Abla. And so he found his way to the small encampment where Bashara had been waylaid, and there he heard the story of strange happenings. So he followed the tracks of the four horses, and he crept up behind a ridge overlooking the silent place and heard 'Abla's voice raised in supplication as she pleaded: 'O Bashara, kill me not, for I am young and in love and would not die. And assuredly by now Shiboob, brother of 'Antar, my beloved, will be upon my heels, and with him perhaps will be my dear servant Rabiat, whom I would welcome here, for she is also my friend, and she too understands the meaning of love for she is enamoured of one who bears your own name, and she might well persuade you not to strike.' And Bashara hesitated, for all his fears of Rabia's revenge, because he found 'Abla's beauty and her tear-drenched eyes quite irresistible, and because, too, she had mentioned his beloved Rabiat. Then, as he paused, lo, a stone flung from a sling over a great distance splintered the silver dagger in his hand, and a second stone felled him to the sand, as the Giant Goliath was once felled by Daoud, king of the wise Jews, so long ago. And he lay helpless, yet he murmured to 'Abla, 'O my mistress, never would I kill you, who have befriended my beloved Rabiat.' And 'Abla thought to herself that, had it not been for her love for Rabiat, she might have perished there in the silent desert, and she shuddered — yet thinking not of herself but of 'Antar's grief.

Now it was arranged with Shiboob, the slinger of stones, that Bashara's mother should shelter 'Abla, who was to be disguised as a boy; and that Bashara should take her clothes, bloodstained, to Rabia as proof of her death while Shiboob sought 'Antar and greeted him, saying:

'Through San'a have I been, and Aden and Zebad and the
    marshes of 'Iraq,
        Seeking her whom thou lovest.

And now, O my brother, I am come with good news,
The breeze is soft, the sun's fierceness is shaded,
The grass grows and is sweet, and the camels feed,
They prosper now, they give good milk, and their young
    are born,
Hope is born where once was sorrow and despair,
        For I have found 'Abla,

'Abla is safe, and our desert world rejoices in her joy.'

And 'Antar's own joy was boundless as the glittering waters which, men say, lie beyond the Great Barrier, the Hejaz.

Rabia, then, and Mufarraj, confident that 'Abla's death had been accomplished, travelled over the wide lands to visit the lord Numan and to try to turn him against Abs. And they left 'Abla's jewels with Numan as a surety of their friendship. Then returning, bearing rich gifts and many camels from this generous leader, Mufarraj left his share with a friend, Malik ibn Hassan, who was no other than Bashara's one-time master.

' '*Antar,*'*Abla and Abjer*'

And Rabia buried his gifts in the sand at Rikaya, and the flocks he turned loose till he could recover them.

But the One Creator whose will is paramount caused 'Antar also to be at Rikaya, as if by chance, and he watched, hidden, while Rabia concealed the gifts and drove the herd to pasture. Then 'Antar possessed himself of them all. And Bashara had news from Malik's men of treasure stored at the camp, and he wrote a letter, supposedly from Mufarraj, and rode to the camp with it, and the letter went thus: 'O Malik, I am called to the aid of the Persian King. Bashara is to load my treasure, and drive my camels, to a secret place'; and Malik was deceived. So that Bashara possessed himself of all. Then, led by Shiboob, he brought 'Abla, still in her boy's clothing, to meet 'Antar at Rikaya, and they headed for home. They separated just a furlong from the camp so that 'Abla could regain her mother's tent unseen. And the leaders of the tribe came out to meet 'Antar and Shiboob, marvelling at the flocks and camels following them, and at the treasure chests with which they were loaded.

Malec also came, and was astounded at the display of wealth; and at 'Antar's good cheer, and the merriment of those who were returning; and he thought to himself, O if my daughter 'Abla were but with them, I too might rejoice, for I loved her; and moreover a part of these riches would come to my own family through her. But to 'Antar he called, in spite and misery, 'O 'Antar, where is your bride?'

Then all were astonished to hear 'Antar's reply, for he cried cheerily, 'Nay, my uncle, is she not where she should be, in her mother's tent, preparing to receive her lover?' And, indeed, as they entered the camp so 'Abla appeared at the black tent's door, clothed in a girl's white robe, and lovely as a moonbeam stealing from behind the clouds on a winter's night. And 'Antar would not pause to explain her presence, but he swept her to his saddle, and so they continued into the camp together, with Bashara and Rabiat, whose joy, too, was unbounded. And all the tribe rejoiced at the return of good fortune and happiness to the lovers, and at Shiboob's gallantry and skill. But Malec went weeping to his tent in confusion, for, though giving thanks for his daughter's escape from the fate which Rabia had planned for her, he realized that in entrusting her jewels to Rabia much of his treasure had been lost, even as his daughter would be lost in marriage to 'Antar.

The Fifteenth Story
'ABLA'S TREASURE RESTORED

When it became known to Rabia that 'Abla had escaped from the net he had spread for her, his anger was dark as the desert is dark at the approach of a dust storm, dry and menacing and blown on the eastern wind. And Rabia vowed vengeance upon Bashara and plotted also to threaten the lord Zuhair himself with the enmity of King Numan. But at the Abs camp the rejoicing lasted many days, until finally Zuhair, in conference with his sons, Shas, Malik the Prince and Qais, summoned 'Antar and Sheddad to discuss with them the retrieval of 'Abla's jewels, which would in honour have to be restored to the tribe. And Rabia's name was muttered in contempt by many, but 'Antar said, in the nobility of his heart, 'Nay, my brothers, he gave way to temptation as many of us have done before now, and if he but admits his guilt we must not condemn him.' And it was at this time that he wrought the famous poem which begins:

'There is a time for passion,
There is a time for forgetting.

O my people, my heart leans towards mercy.'

'Abla's father and her brother also approached the lord Zuhair about the jewels, and Zuhair sent Qais to negotiate privately with Rabia, hoping to hide from other tribes the disgrace which Rabia had brought upon them all.

Now Rabia was a witty and resourceful man, and when he was challenged by Qais over the question of the jewels he asked, 'Why, uncle, what have I to do with this? Ask my fair cousin if she can swear to seeing me either at the lakeside where you say she was abducted, or at the meeting place where last her jewels were seen. She is honesty itself, and I have no fear of her answer.' But Bashara spoke up before Zuhair, saying, 'My lord, there is confusion here. For although the two men who set upon me were muffled and spoke but little, it happened that when the fair 'Abla was sheltering in my mother's tent disguised as a youth, and when I sought out Rabia and found him and Mufarraj, they had discarded their kefiyehs, and I showed them the bloodstained clothes 'Abla had been wearing, stained now with the blood of a sheep, and I could see the evil pleasure gleaming in Rabia's eyes, and indeed I shrank before it.' And all believed him.

Then Rabia and his men left camp to avoid further trouble, but fighting nevertheless took place between him and those who supported 'Antar, and all was shame, chaos and animosity. But Zuhair finally resumed authority, and he forced Qais to expel Rabia, and commanded that Shas expel 'Antar; but as can be imagined, 'Antar had already left in rage and anguish at the whole ignoble affray.

With him travelled Bashara, carried in a litter after injury in the combat, and Rabiat to care for him, and Sheddad, and 'Abla and her mother Sheriya, and many others, and they repaid Rabia for his trouble-making by capturing flocks belonging to the Zaiyad and Fazara people. Yet tempers cooled: and finally a conference was held at Rikaya. 'Antar decided to approach Numan on the matter of the jewels, and to harass those who had aided Rabia in 'Abla's capture. And Shiboob recommended the safety of the valley Raml, high in the mountain Radm, as a base for this venture. 'For this is a country,' said Shiboob, 'in which we can find safe shelter, and also a bountiful supply of fodder, and even of firewood, and game and birds of many kinds for our nourishment.' And sure enough, after many days, they came upon the Great River, and far beyond it the wooded hill slopes of 'Iraq, and here they installed themselves in the Raml valley, burning a swathe of trees to render themselves safe from attack. And the fires burned for six days.

When all was secure, and the camp surrounded by a fair

space to discourage reckless invaders, 'Antar travelled on with a hundred and fifty men to seek Mufarraj and the Shaban, leaving Sheddad with but a few men to guard the camp.

Thus was Abs divided by strife and distance, and worse was to come. For Mufarraj learned of the trick by which he had lost his treasure, and his hatred of Bashara and of the Abs almost choked him. He determined to enlist the support of Numan and to fight Zuhair. And war might have followed immediately had it not been that, about this time, the lord Numan learned of the incomparable beauty of Mutajerida, daughter of Zuhair and Temadhur, and Numan desired her for his wife.

Numan was influenced by Mufarraj's anger, which was bitter as water from the Dead Sea, when he received news also of Abla's escape. And Numan addressed a letter to Zuhair, couched in haughty and undiplomatic terms:

Sire,

We are told by our friend Mufarraj that his property has been filched from him by a trick, and that the perpetrator of this trick, the slave Bashara, is under your protection. We request that you therefore hand over the slave and restore the property of our friend; and it is our wish that the transfer be made by your own tribe's servant, 'Antar the Negro, who is said to have cooperated with the slave Bashara in robbing one who enjoys our protection.

Once this affair is settled, we would approach you, Sire, upon a happier issue, for it is our desire to bind the ties between our two peoples through marriage with your daughter, Mutajerida, of whose beauty we have often heard.

When you have complied with our requests, we will consider any demand you may make for a brideprice for your daughter.

Now the arrogance of this letter affronted the lord Zuhair, and he replied briefly that he had no daughter available for marriage, and that, had he had one, he would not send her so far from home. Nor did he know anything of the property of Numan's protégé, Mufarraj. He added that his noble nephew 'Antar was away from the camp, and he sent Numan's messenger home with nothing but a present of clothing to show for all the long journey and the arrogant demands.

And now the armies of the desert were on the move, for

Zuhair advanced against Numan. Rabia enlisted his friends, Hadifa from the Fazara country, and Dhalim ibn Harith of the Murra tribe (he who wielded the great sword Dhu al Hayat, 'the Lord of Life', heirloom of Juban ibn Himyar, ruler of the universe). Rabia intended supporting Numan against both Zuhair and 'Antar; and Mufarraj was ready to join him in the battles to come. And on Numan's side also was his valiant brother Aswad. But Numan's resolve was weakened by his desire to marry Mutajerida. And Zuhair's and 'Antar's forces were weakened by separation.

So it was that Rabia and Mufarraj were enabled, with a band of men, to steal unperceived in to the sandy Raml valley, where Sheddad guarded the camp. And when 'Antar and his men returned one evening from a foray with Numan's scouts, they found no cheerful welcome. They found only emptiness, and the sound of the warm wind blowing over the aromatic turf; and on the tallest tree the body of Bashara, the beautiful slave, was hanged. And already it had been half devoured by the wheeling vultures.

There was an evil about Bashara's passing which shocked them all. And they were aghast to find that 'Abla and all the women, together with Sheddad and his few fighting men, were gone. And afterwards the story was told — how Rabia and Mufarraj had surprised the camp, and had avenged themselves in the hanging of Bashara, and how a greater enemy, sent to the valley by Numan, had then come upon them. Ma'adi Kereb, friend and supporter of the widowed Jaida whom 'Antar had wronged, and Jaida herself commanding a fine force. Rabia and Mufarraj had fled and escaped, but Sheddad and the Abs women were taken, and Jaida beat her captives soundly before heading east for Hira. And, indeed, troubles fell thick upon Abs, for the lord Zuhair, leading his forces into battle against Numan's main army under Aswad, was captured with his fighting men and his old men, his women and children, and his servants, for he had had none to spare guarding camp and all were with him. So of all the Abs tribe, only 'Antar and a small force were free men.

And now, O my listeners, we hear of the Battle of the Pools of Akhrem. Aswad brought his great host, and his Abs prisoners, across the desert route, and he sent men before him on fast camels to bring water back to the main army. But Shiboob, with a few followers, slipped in among them by night and slit

113

the waterskins. Then Aswad sent a second party of men, but these were by now enfeebled by thirst, and 'Antar seized them and their arms and their camels and their waterskins, and 'Antar rode by a roundabout way to the rear of Aswad's army. And there he freed, and refreshed, and armed Zuhair and his men. Whereupon Aswad's men had to sue for peace if they were to obtain safety and water for survival. Ma'adi Kereb came to their aid indeed, but he and 'Antar settled the differences between them in single combat, and they fought as knights should fight, and parted in friendship and respect, with honour satisfied.

It seemed now that power was balanced between Numan and the Abs. Numan held 'Abla and her jewels, and Sheriya and Sheddad and other noble men and women. Yet his desire for Mutajerida offset his triumph. Zuhair, with 'Antar's help, had defeated Numan's main army under Aswad — yet he longed in secret to wed his daughter to such a noble and powerful ally. But enmity still lay between the forces, for Numan was ignorant of Rabia's duplicity and his heart was bitter against 'Antar to whom his father, Mundhir, had shown such generosity over the flying camels. Yet he was a statesman, and he offered now to exchange his prisoners (despite Jaida's protests) for Aswad and his men-at-arms. And this was arranged. But so grim was 'Antar's wrath that, releasing the captives, he stripped them and sent them forth, bare foot, bare headed and naked, even cropping their hair. And, moreover, he gave them no sustenance for their journey to Hira.

Among these men was Dhalim of the Murra tribe, whose son, Harith, was to bring tragedy to all, and 'Antar might indeed have acted less savagely had he known the outcome of his deeds. But the One God in mercy and justice hides the future from our blind eyes.

Numan's heralds reproached 'Antar for causing such shame, but 'Antar rebuked them even more strongly for the ignorance behind their enmity and for their constant abuse. And Shiboob, in furious indignation, produced an old wreck of a camel for Prince Aswad, who, as furiously, refused it. And so the humiliated prisoners reached Hira, and Numan feared that Chosroes would assuredly choose another than himself to subdue these fiery desert men.

Zuhair and his forces, with 'Abla safe, the jewels recovered and honour restored, could not yet return home since Numan's armies were still strong enough to bar the way. So he retired to the Valley of the Torrents. Then, gradually, tempers cooled, and only Aswad's shame and anger lay like a shadow between the opponents. Then Aswad captured Sheddad, and would have killed him in Numan's presence. Yet did the lord Numan hesitate, and he released Sheddad, and sent him with secret messages to Zuhair, and Zuhair summoned 'Antar, saying, 'Here, now, is a chance of a truce between our armies, and of peace, strengthened by marriage, between two peoples.' And 'Antar replied, 'O my lord, Numan has released my father and subdued my pride by his liberality. As for your daughter, she must surely marry, and could find no nobler match than King Numan, vice-regent to the Emperor Chosroes Nushirvan.'

So it was settled, and the animosity between the two peoples dissipated with the realization of the true causes of their quarrels. Only Aswad could not face his conqueror 'Antar, and he departed to live among the Fazara, there marrying Miriam, sister of Hadifa, their leader. And there appeared to be peace between Fazara and Abs, but it was a hollow peace.

Then Zuhair at last agreed to the marriage of Numan with his daughter, Mutajerida, and he led his tribe back to their own grazing lands — eager, all of them, to celebrate the marriage of the noble warrior 'Antar to his fair cousin 'Abla. And among the tribes this year is known as the year of the two marriages.

The Sixteenth Story

THE SECOND ABDUCTION
AND THE MARRIAGE

When Numan's marriage feasts were over and he and Mutajerida had become man and wife, Zuhair began the long journey home; but between him and his safe return was raised a barrier seemingly as high and insurmountable as are the great sand reefs of the Empty Quarter. For Chosroes sent a force against Numan, and Aswad was sought and given his brother's place as leader. Rabia and Hadifa fought with Aswad against Abs, and Abs supported Numan in his need. Numan, though he had seemingly lost all, was comforted by the prophecies of Dhuraid ibn Sama, who was at this time already four hundred years old and who, it is said, survived to see the Prophet himself, upon whose name be peace.

The desert armies, and the armies of Hira and of Chosroes, met and clashed in many battles in these harsh times, and when the main battle was engaged the fighting continued for eight days, and it is said that the very angels in paradise wept over all, for there were noble men on either side.

But at last Dhuraid's soothsaying proved true. Numan, aided by Zuhair and 'Antar, resumed leadership, forgiving his brother Aswad; and Chosroes's gallant general, Khodawend, returned to tell the emperor that his interests were safeguarded still, and to instruct him, doubtless, on the feuds and jealousies of the Zaiyad which had sparked off so great a war. So it came about that the lands were ruled, as they had been before, with Chosroes depending upon Numan, and Numan upon Zuhair and the other desert leaders, in good faith and honesty.

And Abs returned to its beloved lands, and all was in readiness for 'Antar's marriage with 'Abla. But one more danger had yet to be faced by the lovers before their happiness was complete.

Malec and his son Amr were captured by one Wakid ibn Mesaar of the Kinan, and Wakid determined to hold them to ransom, seeing that they were men of worth and standing; but Amr, who had always hated his sister, thought to use her for his release, and he spoke to Wakid of her great beauty and her wit and her many virtues, and Wakid hungered after 'Abla. So he kept Malec's men as hostages, and he said to Malec, 'Go now with your son, and fetch me your daughter 'Abla here, that I may marry her, for I am told she is as beautiful as the moon itself. Your men will remain here,' continued Wakid, 'and if you do not return with 'Abla I will kill them with great cruelty, and you yourselves will never feel secure for my men are skilled at tracking, and if you do not return with 'Abla they will hunt you down when you least expect it, and will kill you. Indeed, I am sending three men with you to act as your shadows, and they will report to me what you do and what you do not do.' So Malec and Amr returned quietly and said nothing of their capture to Sheriya and her daughter 'Abla; and they made excuses for the absence of their men, saying that they had come across much game and had left the men to watch both animals and birds. Then, on a pretext, after a few days they persuaded 'Abla and her mother to ride with them to the foothills, and there, by arrangement, they fell in with Wakid's men and were recaptured. For Wakid's men had followed Malec and Amr from afar off and had made sure that their leader's wishes were obeyed.

Then 'Abla, realizing her plight, wept before her father, who cried: 'Dry your tears, my daughter, for the weight of such grief would crush the mountains themselves'; and 'Abla turned upon him, saying, 'O my unworthy father, it was you who did plan to kill my beloved 'Antar, and you who have now rendered me a captive. May injustice fall upon your own head. For there is One who deals out justice and retribution.' Then Amr spoke up, saying to Wakid, 'Here is your bride, take her and take care, too, that she falls in with your desires, for she is wayward as well as beautiful.' Whereupon 'Abla, enraged, cursed her brother, and he set upon her with a whip for he could not bear her curses and her reproaches, and above all her mockery. But Wakid admired her spirit and prevented Amr's cowardly behaviour. So the party continued over the desert, with 'Abla and her mother riding as captives in litters; and 'Abla refused all food, and the two women cursed their menfolk as they rode, crying by day, 'God will bring retribution upon you,' and by night weeping together.

So it came as almost a relief to Malec and Amr, and to Wakid himself, when they were accosted by a party of armed slaves serving Tericat el Zeman of the Beni Riyan, a tribe of murderers and adulterers, men who had no respect for the virtue or worth of women as have the men of Abs, and indeed all other Arab tribes. And Wakid, thinking to please 'Abla, said to her, 'O my fair 'Abla, see how easily will I rescue you from these adulterers.' But he was killed.

Now, in the confusion of the battle, 'Abla's quick eyes had spied a dagger lying on the stony ground, and she picked it up and whispered to her mother, 'We may yet save ourselves' — and so it was, for although Malec and Amr were captured by the Beni Riyan, and held bound as hostages, 'Abla and Sheriya were able to cut the ropes secretly at night, although so great was their rage that they debated whether they should come to the aid of such worthless men. But once the rescue was effected, and all four had escaped on stolen horses, Sheriya thought to herself, We were right to help them, for we are of one blood.

It happened that as they journeyed they fell in with Rabia and Amara returning from the hunt, and the two parties conferred about the feelings of the tribe — should they return, or should they depart for ever from their own people, having brought upon themselves so much hatred and scorn? And 'Abla, Sheriya and Malec were for returning, but Rabia, Amara and Amr were in favour of flying to a new country. But they were careless of their safety, and they were once more surprised and captured by a party of armed men led by Tericat himself. And now the four Abs men were bound again as prisoners, and Tericat, who thought only of lust (to him a passing passion, for he had no knowledge of the refinements of love), desired 'Abla and ordered that she be taken in a litter to a secret valley where water abounded and where he would be hidden and might fulfil his desires whether she were willing or no. And 'Abla left Tericat in no doubt as to her feelings, cursing him as she was carried off in the litter; but the desert breezes swept the sound away, and the slaves were deaf both to her anger and her weeping.

Tericat sat down with his followers to eat, full of fantasy and picturing to himself the delights awaiting him in the secret valley. But there was among the Absians one who knew every secret of the desert: Shiboob, brother of 'Antar, who had been searching for 'Abla since her disappearance with her father, mother and brother so many long days before. It was as though they had all been swallowed up in one of the great dust storms, those which blow for three days, or five days, and in which many lives are lost. Yet Shiboob believed 'Abla to be alive, and he, with 'Antar, was combing every hill and every wadi, guided by the One who brings retribution and reward; and they had come together to the secret valley, and from a hiding place watched the slaves drop down from the crest and set down 'Abla's litter on the flat sands by the springs. And they saw 'Abla dismount and refresh herself at the springs while the slaves pitched camp for their master, and they heard 'Abla's sighs and complaints and observed the tears coursing down her pale cheeks, for it was many days since she had eaten properly. Then, at the sight of her tears, Shiboob and 'Antar rose from their hiding place, terrible in aspect, and descended upon the slaves and rescued 'Abla and comforted her.

Later in the day came Tericat to the valley, full of desire and careless of his safety — for were not his slaves and his fighting men around him? But one of the slaves, whose life had been spared by 'Antar as he was but a boy, struggled towards Tericat, crying, 'O my master, the lovely Abs girl is already in the hands of a black monster, and my fellow slaves are dead men.' Tericat hissed in rage like a horned viper on the sand-dunes, and he leaped forward like a hyena to challenge 'Antar. And they fought there in the secret valley.

Behind the crest of the hill, Malec and Amr, Rabia and Amara, heard their blows and shouting while they themselves lay bound upon the stony ground and wondered what their own fate would be. And Sheriya heard them too, yet she wondered what would be her daughter's fate at the end of it all, for none could see anything. Then 'Antar felled Tericat to the ground, and Tericat cried, 'Come, O Negro, I can see you are valiant and strong. Join forces with me and my companions, and we will roam the wilderness together like the broad-winged kites which soar in the sky seeking their prey. We will absent ourselves from those chiefs who call us slaves, and who boast of their lineage, and we will live on the plunder we amass, and the prisoners we capture in the lonely places.' But 'Antar would not, for he was a proud man and could not unite himself with a band of robbers who murdered for pleasure and disregarded the honour of women. So he killed Tericat.

Then went 'Antar and Shiboob to release Sheriya and to re-unite her with her daughter, and they set free also Malec and Amr, Rabia and Amara, and most courteously greeted them and congratulated them; and the only reproach 'Antar allowed himself was to say quietly to Malec, 'Did you not deceive your daughter and myself in attempting to force a marriage outside the betrothal we had pledged, and is it not through this that you have fallen into distress and humiliation? O my uncle, this has been the punishment for injustice.' And Shiboob wondered at 'Antar's courtesy, but 'Antar said to him, 'We must not bear malice, O my brother, we must renounce it; for no good ever came of malice. Violence, too, is infamous, its results are ever uncertain and no one can do justice when driven by hatred or revenge. Let us bear with evil, and let our patience endure.' Then all returned to the valley, and when a meal was ready, 'Antar served the four men with his own hands and shamed them greatly by his fair manners, so that Rabia and Amara and Amr hated him even more, yet shame and jealousy rendered them silent. Evil smouldered still within their hearts, and the remembrance of every wicked action of their own added fuel to the burning of their detestation. The three of them decided between themselves that night that Amr must leave the tribe and fly to Yemen. 'For remember,' Rabia said, 'how the people reacted to 'Antar's supposed death. He is their hero, and 'Abla is his beloved, and 'Abla will not forget your crimes, O Amr, or against her mother, or against the tribe, or against herself, in which matters you have acted in a most unbrotherly manner.' And Amr wept with rage.

But Malec felt some remorse for his evil actions and he helped 'Antar to guard the camp overnight, and to keep Sheriya and 'Abla safe. So after two days the wanderers returned to camp and were welcomed; but Amr was not with them, nor was he seen again for many months, and when he did return he was changed, and he was forgiven, but that is another story. And Rabia and Amara, though welcome among their own men and families, were looked upon with suspicion by the people of Abs.

But for 'Antar and 'Abla, and for Sheriya, the welcome of the people of Abs was a welcome of love, and for many days all was happiness, and the feasting and music and dancing lasted late and long into the starry nights. Now there was time to rejoice in the reunion of the two lovers, and time too to marvel at the riches 'Antar had brought to his beloved from the far lands of the east. There was time to appreciate the almost stupefying grandeur of his gifts, and time to listen, over and over again, to the strange and delightful stories of Mundhir's encampments and cities, of the beauties of Hira; of Chosroes's gardens and palaces, and of his food and wine; of the battles with the Patrician and with Bahram. Time, too, to hear once more of the strange Christian monks who had tried to save the Governor of Antioch from his due payment of tribute; of the marvellous rites of the Fireworshippers, shown and explained to 'Antar by Mubidan before he left the Persian hills. Time, now, to reflect upon stories of the Emperor who lived far beyond Antioch, even; and of the Virgin's son, Issa, who had come to set the world to rights; and of the wise Jews who had, none the less, lost Jerusalem to the Romans.

And on the grazing lands around the camp the thousand flying camels, now quite at home, moved out to crop the grass and flowers, each with its long shadow so that they resembled a great multi-coloured carpet thrown upon the land. For their colours ranged from white to gold, and from gold to copper, and so to black, and they seemed to fly over the desert on strong legs and velvet feet making no more noise than does an owl flitting across the silver sands by moonlight. Their trim bodies and humps were rounded and full, and their woolly coats were soft as velvet, and they moved to the sound of a thousand bells.

'Abla wore and displayed her clothes and ornaments, and all the tribe benefited from her kindness and from 'Antar's generosity. And Amara's love for 'Abla burned within him when he saw her beauty enhanced by such rich stuffs and such glowing jewels. Three times he had tried to delay or to prevent her marriage with 'Antar. Once he had abducted her after trapping her by a false message which brought her to the desert's edge alone and at night. But Shiboob had foiled this plan, for he kept constant watch. Once Amara had introduced into the keeping of 'Abla's servants a poisoned herb, a few drops from which would have cast her into a slumber like death itself, his hope being that he might drive 'Antar to suicide in his grief, and that he himself might snatch 'Abla as from the very tomb. But this plot too was frustrated when his own servant warned 'Abla's maidens, and they in turn introduced the juice of the herb into Amara's wine, so that he lay on the brink of death. Finally he had sought to stop the marriage by asserting that 'Abla and 'Antar could not wed, since they were milk sister and milk brother to each other, having been suckled by the same slave. But this was easily disproved, for was it not well remembered that 'Antar was seven years old when Sheriya gave birth to 'Abla, and was that not the year of the great rains? And had not 'Antar been fourteen years old when 'Abla had sought his help in mastering the desert ponies she so loved to ride, and was that not the year in which a party of Nabateans had come from their rock city, seeking information about those who could supply spices from the far Yemen?

In due course the tribe turned upon Amara and mocked him, assuring him that his love for 'Abla had turned his brain, and it might be well, they said, if he could take himself off until he recovered his wits. So he too left with his men; and Rabia left with him, and neither was greatly regretted, though they stayed away many seasons.

Then 'Antar and 'Abla were at last united, and their great love became a legend in that part of Arabia; and their wealth, generosity and virtues, and 'Antar's poetry, are remembered to this day. The Prince and Sheddad, father of 'Antar, and Samiya, Sheddad's wife, and all the rest are well remembered for their part in these stories, and all the stories which follow — the tales of 'Antar's further adventures. For he proved himself to be a hero and a true Arab, faithful to his God, liberal in his hospitality, sincere in his promises. And 'Abla had already proved her faithfulness, and shown her brave spirit in adversity and her forgiveness in triumph. For she respected her father in his old age, despite all he had done to harm her.

And 'Antar continued to weave magic verses about his lovely bride, of whom he caused this to be written at the time of their marriage:

'She plays with men's hearts.

It is as though the moon had dropped down among us,
        What else can we see?

She comes, supple as a willow branch.
When she decks herself with jewels it is as though
The Seven Stars had come to sparkle at her throat,
El Thurayya had come to cluster on her bosom,
    The misty stars,
    The centre of the universe.'*

And when his poem first was heard at the time of the marriage, the heart of Malec was melted, and he replied to it thus:

'Now may he marry whom he pleases.
It is the wish of all the tribe.

What valour he has shown, how noble have been
    His motives throughout the years,
      How steadfast his desires.

The Beni Abs depend now upon strong foundations:
    The one — the lord Zuhair,
    The other — O my son 'Antar.

Thy father Sheddad — whom God preserve — O 'Antar,
Son of my brother, husband of my daughter 'Abla.'

And Malec would indeed have kissed his nephew's feet, but 'Antar prevented him and embraced him, saying, 'O my uncle, this I will not suffer, for was I not a slave and a herder of camels?' And Malec answered, 'Noble knight, all the dangers into which I have thrown you were devised only to give you the opportunity of acquiring this renown, this high degree of glory, so that without shame I could give 'Abla, daughter of a noble line, to him who led my brother's camels to pasture.'

And 'Antar and 'Abla smiled to each other at the words of the old man.

*El Thurayya, or the 'Misty Stars': these are the Pleiades.

The Seventeenth Story
HARITH'S LOVE FOR LABNA

Once in the days when peace was restored between Chosroes and Numan, and between Numan and his brother Aswad, 'Antar and his friends Urwa and Hijar were riding south from Hira, heading for home.

They left behind them the great sliding river, the palm trees and the shade and the fertile gardens where violets grow as big as roses, and roses as big as thornbushes; and they could no longer hear the nightingale and the dove and the bulbul singing among the pomegranate bushes, nor see the hoopoe, the absent one, messenger between Suleiman and Bilquis, flitting over the green grass. They passed over the cornfields to the desert's edge, and soon left even the partridges and quails and the chequered sand-grouse behind them, and the barred bustard, too heavy a prey for their hunting hawks.

And the desert men and their strong horses rejoiced as stubble and aromatic turf gave way to rising ground, bare rock and firm sand, and they rode faster and thought themselves safer in this empty world where a man may see his enemy and his friend, and where God watches over all. It happened that the little group of men and horses felt so exultant as the great landscape widened before them, boundless, beautiful and coloured as the very roses of 'Iraq, that they became careless; and with nightfall they lay unguarded by the dying embers of their fires, and they slept, horses and men close together, under the wheeling stars.

Now they had travelled but a short day's journey from the

124

desert's edge, and as they left the sown land they were perceived by a company of robbers who were given to attacking any unwary travellers at the riverside, or in the date gardens near by, and who lay close in the scrub growing between the cultivation and the dry uplands. There were forty thieves in this company, and they lay silent as the men of Abs passed by; then followed, taking cover among the bushes as far as they were able, and then among the rocks, and the sandhills, until it became apparent that the travellers were intent upon the tracks before them and cast no backward glances at the lands they left without reluctance. And as 'Antar reined his horse Abjer to snuff the wind and determine which way would lead them home, the leader of the thieves turned to his men and whispered, 'We have little need of caution among these desert men whose hearts and eyes are fixed upon the southern road. Let us await the dark, then I and four others will steal in among them and will return with forty horses, and the leader's horse will be my own, for never have I seen an animal to equal it: black as night sky yet polished like a basalt stone from Mafraq, his ears straight and pricked like a reed pen.' And so it happened that when the violet dusk was dimmed, and the night fallen, and men and horses slept, five of the thieves padded over the firm sand to 'Antar's camp where he lay asleep with his friends and his men, and they rounded up the horses, and so skilful were they, and so gentle, that even Abjer allowed himself to be taken and led away; for it seemed to him that the men spoke his own language.

Yet was Abjer uneasy, and when of a sudden he was led into the robbers' camp where torches blazed among the high rocks and all was noise and flurry, Abjer's wide nostrils flared like the black petals of an iris from Madiba, and he reared high, striking with his hoofs the leader of the thieves, who then lay dead upon the sand. And Abjer fled.

Thus, in the dim light before dawn 'Antar, his friends and his men watched in wonder as Abjer sped over the rippling sand towards them like a dark star sliding on a pale sky.

It happened that 'Antar and his men were travelling to meet Harith ibn Zuhair, seventh son of the lord Zuhair, and, some said, the most beloved of his father, and of his mother, Temadhur. Now Harith was a young man, and beautiful, and the favourite, too, of his sister Mutajerida, she who was renowned for her wit, her common sense and great beauty,

'Harith and Labna'

and who was the consort of the King Numan in Hira. Harith
had left the Abs camp some days before our story was begun,
and in the far desert he camped with but a few followers,
waiting for 'Antar and the others. But they did not come.

Then did Harith strike off on his own to hunt in an unknown
part of the wilderness, and he was led astray by a gazelle's
fawn. The fawn leapt ahead of Harith and was lost to view on
the far side of a ridge of dunes, and Harith galloped in pursuit and drove his horse stumbling up the ridge till it reached
the summit and stood panting among the coarse grasses and
crumbling sand. And then were both Harith and his horse
filled with delicious longing, for Harith saw before him a
maiden of surpassing beauty, and the horse saw the glitter of
fresh water and smelled the sweet softness of it in the desert air.

Now the maiden made as if to run startled down the white
sand to the water's edge, but Harith slipped from his horse and
held out his hand as if to an unbroken colt, whispering:

> 'What magic now is this?
> My horse and I were fast upon the heels of a swift fawn,
>> A gazelle — light as the air it was,
>>> Or foam upon the wind,
> And it was lost to us over the dunes.
>
>> Yet when we top the dunes,
>> We find fairer far than our fawn,
>>> A maiden whose grey eyes mirror the waters of the lake,
>>>> Dark under winter clouds,
>>>> A maiden whose shining hair
>> Ripples both dark and red, like copper in the firelight.
>
>>> Has then some magic changed our fleet gazelle
>>>> Into a princess?'

Then, listening to these words, the maiden answered in
verses as ardent as those of her discoverer:

>> 'No magic brings me here.
>> Only the gods perhaps answering my prayer.
>
>>> For I come here to the dunes,
>> High on the dunes each day above the lake,
>> I look out over the waters where my companions play,

I look for my loved one, he whom I have never seen,
   Save in my mind, till now.'

And indeed love flared between Harith and the maiden, as the camp fire flares when a dry thornbush draws new life from the embers and the sparks fly up to vie with the very stars.

Now the name of the maiden was Labna, and her father was Bekr ibn Moatemid, a leader among the Zohran tribe; and she and her friends would come each day to the lake to play and bathe in the clear waters which were strange to them, for they came from afar off and had sought and found new grazing. And Labna was wooed by her cousin Jarir ibn Qadim, and of this match Bekr was disapproving, so he had joined those who sought and found the new grazing. Every day Labna would climb to the ridge overlooking the lake, and she would dream of the lover who could satisfy her more surely than Jarir her cousin. Indeed, it seemed to Labna that Harith came directly from her dream, and the two could not be parted, though both feared the dangers of their chance discovery. So they arranged that Harith should send for his old nurse to act as a go-between, and after a few days she joined Labna in the Zohran camp, pretending to be a gipsy, and Labna's friends laughed at them both for their closeness, but did not question Labna when she and the old woman walked or rode each day to a little shelter, built now upon the ridge, beneath the erak trees.

There in the little shelter the lovers met in secret, during many days, as if in a dream of magic quality.

But one day when Harith slipped over the dunes to his little pavilion of reeds, taken from the lake, he found his nurse weeping and alone, for the Zohran people had been summoned home by their overlord, Ashath ibn Dhahra, who needed his flocks and his men elsewhere, and who had seized Jarir ibn Qadim. Ashath had determined that Labna should marry Kheitoor, one who had already proffered a good bride-price in Bekr's absence. And Bekr was delighted with this new offer for his daughter, but Labna wept, for the betrothal was to take place in only ten days' time.

Then did Labna summon up her courage, and she said to herself, 'I cannot submit to this marriage, for my heart is a captive elsewhere.' And she sought out a camel more silent than the rest, and secretly she saddled the beast unobserved, and she loaded it with a few belongings and slipped away in the darkness over the way she now knew so well, back to her lover, Harith ibn Zuhair.

When, in the morning, her absence was discovered, there was dismay and disturbance, and into this troubled camp rode Shiboob, seeking Harith and riding upon a pack-horse, one of the few left to 'Antar and his party after the theft of all their good horses by the forty thieves. And Shiboob was disguised as a beggar.

Now it occurred to Shiboob that if Labna had left her people because of the marriage ceremonies arranged for her, she must surely have left for love of some other lover, and he circled the Zohran encampment and found the tracks of Labna's silent camel leading off towards the lake; and indeed the lake had been the meeting place for 'Antar and Harith, only they were to have met on the further shore. Then did Shiboob reckon that his brother's cousin might need help against the Zohran if he should turn out to be Labna's lover, and Shiboob bargained for a swifter horse and set off in pursuit of Labna. And sure enough he came upon the two lovers, who had met half-way to the lake, for Harith, crazy with anxiety, had followed the tracks alone and virtually unarmed, for is it not said that love steals a man's senses from him as easily as the unshaded sun at noonday?

No sooner had Shiboob hastily warned the young people of pursuit, than dust arose to the east and a band headed by Kheitoor and Bekr galloped across the flat sand. And Shiboob seized the bridle of Labna's camel and urged it westwards towards some low hills which might serve as a refuge; and when the camel was spent, Shiboob took Labna on his saddle-bow, and Harith spurred his horse, and together they galloped for safety. And when the horses too were spent, Shiboob carried Labna in his arms up the stony cliffs, and Harith struggled behind them, thinking to himself, Truly this man knows the desert as well as any jinn, and some say indeed that he is descended from among these spirits. And the three came upon a secret place, well guarded by rocks and with shade from the sun, and from here Shiboob could keep the pursuers at bay, for he was well armed with bow and arrows and could shoot as surely as the Great Archer himself.

Now the pursuit consisted of only twenty men, for they expected no resistance and wished only to recapture Labna and her camel. And from the rocky hilltop Shiboob and Karith could see that the hunters how themsleves were hunted, for a band of armed men appeared from the north, and while Kheitoor's troop was advancing up the steep places on foot, the armed men surrounded the Zohran horses waiting below, and drove them off. And it was indeed the forty thieves who did this act.

But their triumph did not last, for on the far horizon Shibbob, Labna and Harith could see a puff of dust; and the golden sunlight of the morning gleamed upon the black sword of 'Antar as he swept in pursuit, mounted upon Abjer, who had escaped from the thieves' den. Shiboob ran like an oryx to the hilltop, and on the summit was a cairn of stones commemorating the death of a traveller who had sheltered there in the caves, but who had surrendered to the Great Hunter who must claim us all — and Shiboob leapt upon the cairn and chose from his quiver a special arrow tipped with eagle feathers from the High Yemen where the white mountains harbour these kings among birds. And Shiboob loosed his arrow, standing against the golden sun, and the arrow sped, they say, further than human strength could send it, and perhaps the gods themselves prolonged its flight. For it fell but a few paces ahead of Abjer, and 'Antar, recognizing his brother's weapon, looked up towards the sun and he saw the three figures and the men of Zohran below them, and the forty thieves making away with the herded horses, and he turned Abjer in among the horses so that all became part of a great stampede, flying perforce up the slopes of the rock-strewn hill.

In the confusion the thieves were dispersed or captured, and Kheitoor was killed, but Labna, her russet hair streaming in the morning breeze, ran from her hiding place to protect her father, Bekr, so that Harith and Shiboob should spare him. And all was then explained to Bekr, who was proud that his lovely daughter should have won the heart of so fine a man as Harith, son of the lord Zuhair — a man befriended, as was apparent, by men of magic and superhuman strength. And Bekr swore to support his daughter's choice against the wishes of his overlord.

So together they drove the horses and the prisoners back to Ashath's domain, where all was once more recounted, and great was the rejoicing in the tribe at Labna's story, though her cousin Jareer was humiliated. And Labna and Harith were escorted to their own country, while 'Antar and Shiboob drove the stolen horses back over the high desert to comfort with their reappearance the Absians who had so carelessly allowed themselves to be outwitted by the forty thieves.

The Eighteenth Story

ASYED AND HIS FAITHFUL SELMA

The name of Asyed is a remembered name, he whose father Jazima was killed in battle by Robab, Queen of the Riyan, who struck him down in the sight of all his tribe, and whom men compare with Zenobia, conqueror of Rome, in the days when Palmyra was still a proud city at the height of its beauty. Yet was Zenobia a captive in the later years, and Robab was slain by the lord Zuhair to avenge his father. And Asyed ibn Jazima was brother to Zuhair, and Asyed was a learned man who could both read and write.

Now it happened that Zuhair was searching in the far desert for his son Harith, and for 'Antar and his men, who were returning from 'Iraq, and Zuhair sent his scouts riding out to the wind's end, and they brought him news of his brother Asyed who was returning from a pilgrimage in to the Sacred Valley, where no blood is shed; and Zuhair set out to meet his brother in the Valley of the Erak Trees.

Now this was a sheltered and a smiling place, and green withal, and here men came in peace to gather the fragrant roots which later the Prophet — peace be upon him — was to recommend to the faithful for use in their ablutions. Zuhair and Asyed then camped together in the Valley of the Erak Trees. Now as they sat there in the firelight, sipping their wine, with evening passing swiftly into night and the clear stars lighting up the whole map of heaven, Asyed spoke sadly to his brother and wept.

Zuhair was astonished by his grief, and Asyed murmured:

'O my brother, here in this sheltered valley,
Midway between the Sacred Groves and our own harsh
  country,
Here, once, long ago, I tasted the joys of love.

Here am I haunted, still, by memories of my brief
  happiness.'

And the story came to be told thus:

Once, many years before, as a young man, Asyed accompanied his father to the Sacred Groves and drank from the spring of Zamzam which flowed for the quenching of Isma'il's thirst. And as they journeyed home they camped in the Valley of the Erak Trees, and the bushes provided shelter for many game birds, and many deer and other beasts moved in the close thickets and nibbled the short grass, for there was water there and shade from the sun's mastery. So when Jazima set off for the west, Asyed, with but a few friends, stayed in the valley to hunt game. It happened that Asyed was a fearless hunter, and one day he outstripped his companions and rode far and dangerously, hunting a savage boar which disappeared into the rock-strewn hilltops where a horse might not follow; and the sun sank in the west, casting long shadows on a strange landscape, and Asyed was lost. Then as the darkness came he spied the glimmer of a fire, and he rode towards its welcome warmth and light.

And indeed he found at the fireside a flame which was to overwhelm him and burn within him for ever, for the tiny camp was the camp of an old sheikh, and with him, herding her flocks, was Selma his daughter, and she was very lovely.

So Asyed stayed with his host and helped Selma care for him, for there were but the two of them, and in the daytime he and Selma would drive the camels out to pasture, and in the evening all would return to the bright fire. And Asyed and Selma loved each other with a love which was to become a legend among the tribes; and to this day they are named among us, and a young man may turn upon his loved one, crying, 'Nay, did you not promise me your love, and did I not believe that you would be faithful, as Selma was faithful to Asyed ibn Jazima? Yet now have you proved fickle as thistle-down blown by every chance breeze.'

Asyed's companions sought and found him, and before

witnesses he and Selma were married, and Asyed gave his own sword as a brideprice to the old man, and to Selma he gave his mother's bracelet, which he hung upon a chain around his neck as a charm, for it was studded with turquoise stones against the evil eye. And it fitted perfectly over Selma's slim hand, and glowed blue against her sun-browned arm.

Soon Asyed and his friends left merrily for home, and he planned to fetch the old sheikh and his daughter in a few days' time. But the gods worked against the two lovers, and Asyed's journey was perilous and long, and all save one of his companions were slain on the way home, for these were harsh times. Then also was Asyed's father slain, so it was many months before Asyed could return to seek for Selma, and behold, when he did so the camp was empty and the ashes cold, and cool breezes from the hilltops had blown both sand and dried leaves over all the tracks, and there was no sign of Selma or of her father or of their camels. And Asyed wept, and his world was empty. Yet did he vow he would look upon no other woman, and this was the sad story he recounted to his brother in the Valley of the Erak Trees.

Now it came afterwards to be known that Selma's father died soon after Asyed's departure, and Selma waited in the valley for her lover but he did not come. And after many days a troop of horsemen from the Kayan tribe rode up to the high slopes of the valley, seeking the wild boar as Asyed had before, and they found Selma and her camels and captured all, and she was forced to ride with them to their own country, under the protection of the Qahtan. But Selma, too, had taken a vow to look upon no other lover, and she refused all advances so fiercely that she was left unmolested and, indeed, it became evident that she was with child. When her son was born she named him Nazih, and they lived, the mother and the boy, under the protection of the Kayan people. And the leader of the Kayan valued Selma, for she was skilled in tending sick camels and became known for her cleverness in rearing calves which might well have died, and preserving she-camels from the dangers of infection. Selma became a wise woman among the Qahtan, and they sought her advice upon many things until it was apparent that she had great influence and even mastery in the tribe.

When Nazih grew strong enough to wield his father's sword, Selma demanded it from her captors and he was taught to use it well. And when he was of an age to ride off with the others, youths and men together, Selma slipped the precious turquoise bracelet from her sun-browned arm, where it gleamed blue as the sky in springtime, and she gave it to Nazih, saying to him, 'O my son, here is my most precious possession for you to wear as an amulet against the evil eye. For this bracelet belonged to your father's own mother, and he gave it to me as a pledge of his faithful love. I have never been faithless to him, and I have confidence he will never have betrayed me.' And Nazih thanked his mother gravely for the gift, since he was a kindly young man, but later, like the Friend of God, he fell upon his face and laughed. And he said in his heart, 'Shall a man be faithful to a woman for fifteen years!' — for he was but a youth and had not yet known true love. But he concealed his mirth from his mother.

In the Valley of the Erak Trees, trouble came upon the Absian camp for Zuhair and Asyed stayed over-long, seduced by the greenery and by shelter from the sun's mastery, and they drank wine together and idled away their time, they and their followers together. So that when they were attacked early one morning by a raiding party of the Kayan, all were taken captive, save Zamba and Warca and a handful of men who fled to the desert to find help and refuge. And Asyed and the lord Zuhair were bound and taken to those among the Kayan people, who were at this season of the year dwelling by the Lake of the Waste-lands. And they were disgraced.

They were brought before the leader, and he was indeed Nazih, who was now a grown man, and so Nazih and his father Asyed met for the first time, yet they did not know it. But Nazih nursed a great bitterness in his heart against all the Abs people, for he believed his father had deserted Selma and he had no faith in the trust she herself had treasured within her heart for twenty years. Moreover, Nazih had by now himself learned the meaning of true love, and so the apparent cruelty of his unknown father seemed even sharper. So Nazih determined to revenge the affront to his mother by punishing these men of Abs.

But indeed the gods thought otherwise — for Selma herself had most skilfully planned the raid, hearing that Absians were lingering in the Valley of the Erak Trees, and she thought to herself, Maybe they are but travellers, yet, if so, I could hear news through them of my dear husband. Or maybe he himself has come to seek me in the high valley. For such was her faith that she, unlike her son, could believe no ill of Asyed.

Yet she risked bringing all to disaster, for while Nazih was questioning Asyed and Zuhair, a troop came galloping to their rescue: the men of Abs, called in from afar by Zamba and Warca, who had met Shiboob and Jarir at the wind's end, and had found 'Antar and his men returning from the marriage celebrations of Harith and Labna.

Then a great fight took place upon the beaches, and the gravel glistened with blood in the sunlight, and horses and men lay dead in the shallow water so that the little waves were ruby red instead of crystal clear. And 'Antar challenged the boy Nazih, and they fought together. Nazih was overpowered, and his sword flew from his hand and fell at the feet of Asyed whose bonds were being severed by Shiboob. And Shiboob caught up the sword, meaning to slay Nazih if 'Antar so directed, but two separate cries assailed his ears, for 'Antar called out, 'Nay my brother, kill him not for he fought well.' And Asyed cried, 'O Shiboob, stay your hand! For assuredly this sword is my sword which I wielded as a young man and left indeed as a brideprice for my beloved Selma.' And, still stiff from his binding, Asyed stumbled to the lake's edge where Nazih lay helpless, and he knelt at his side, and he saw fastened around the young man's neck by a golden chain a tiny bracelet studded with blue stones, powerful against the evil eye; and a pledge of faithfulness between two lovers now past their prime. And he whispered, 'Nazih, I beg of you, tell me who is your father. For this is the bracelet I gave to my wife Selma twenty years ago as a pledge of faithfulness.' And Nazih raised himself upon his elbow, and replied, 'My mother's name is indeed Selma, sir, and she has remained faithful to her husband for twenty years and more. But, O stranger, though I have pestered her throughout my youth, yet would she not reveal his name.' And this had indeed been so, for Selma had foreseen the inner thoughts of a young man, as they might grow and darken; and she had in this way prevented a vengeance killing.

But in any case the name seemed immaterial to 'Antar and to Zuhair, and to the men of Abs and to the men of Kayan, for did not the older man and the younger resemble each other as a man and his reflection in still water?

So it was that joy came upon the combatants, and they

ceased from fighting, calling to their fellows, 'Put up your bright swords, for we have no quarrel now among us, but only cause for merriment and feasting.'

So the two parties rode happily together to the main camp, and Asyed heard from his son of the years which had brought so much grief to Selma and her lover, and of Nazih's desire for revenge, and of Selma's unswerving faithfulness. Nazih indeed regarded his father with respect, for here too was a faithful lover who had looked upon no other woman, and Nazih could now share the nobility of this principle. 'For,' he told his father, 'I am myself enamoured of Dhymia, daughter of Obad of the Beni Temim, and I can now see, from the depths of my love, that it is possible for a man to remain faithful to a woman for fifteen or twenty years, or indeed for a lifetime.' And his father rejoiced, observing the young man's fervour. So were Asyed and Selma reunited and all was celebration.

Now some say that Nazih and Dhymia were married at this time. But others say, O my listeners, that Selma went to seek Dhymia at the camp of Obad her father, and that both the women were captured on the return journey by Nacmeh ibn Ashter, lord of Sawda, who ruled the territories surrounding the mountain of Ghemam. Now Ghemam is a fire mountain, and is black in colour, and every month, at the time of the new moon, fire floods from the mountain top, and rivers of fire spill down the blackened slopes to the fertile land below, and ashes darken the sky. Nacmeh's heart was black as the rocks he claimed as his homeland, and he desired Dhymia and arranged for her abduction. But disaster followed, for Nacmeh's son Kelboon, a brave and good man, was killed in the abduction of Dhymia. And when news of this came to Nacmeh, he slaughtered the bearer of the news with his own hand. But Kelboon's brother Niamet mourned for him.

Now Nacmeh was a monstrous man, and evil, yet had the Great Creator given him two noble sons, and the second son, Niamet, arose now against his father and sought help to destroy him even from the Abs and Kayan peoples; for Niamet, like the Prince, abjured violence and oppression, trying always to find a peaceful way out of the quarrels his fellow men persistently indulged in. But Nacmeh had always remained deaf to Niamet's pleas. At this time he had begun to indulge in obnoxious amorous pursuits with maidens whom he seized from neighbouring tribes, and Niamet's shame drove him to action. Besides the Abs and Kayan tribes who had suffered at Nacmeh's hands, Niamet rallied men from the Riyan, the Sabah, the Washash and many others, men whose womenfolk had been insulted and misused by his father.

It was a great assembly, and the leaders were told that the Sawda peoples would worship on the Ghemam mountain in the dark days between the last of the old moon and the first sight of the new, and when messengers came to Nacmeh telling him of his son's defection, the moon had barely risen and the black rocks of the mountain were quaking and throbbing as the subterranean fires welled up to the summit; and Nacmeh left his worship and gathered his armies on the plain of Khidret, which is watered by the springs of Hijwan. And there a battle was joined between Nacmeh and a small force of fighting men, each one of whom Nacmeh had wronged. And this force was led by 'Antar, and by Asyed his uncle, and by Nazih, Asyed's newly discovered son, who fought bravely with the rest. On the second day the strong purpose of 'Antar's forces weighed down the balance on the side of justice, and Nacmeh was killed by 'Antar, and many of Nacmeh's men acknowledged Niamet as their leader, for they had been ashamed of their previous leader's barbarity. And Niamet, in gratitude, gave 'Antar and his men two thousand slaves, and she-camels of a very patient breed which flourish among these people of the fire mountain.

But to Nazih he gave no camels, only the fair Dhymia, rescued from her captivity and unharmed; and to Asyed he restored his wife Selma; and together the faithful pair joined in the celebrations with the two young people.

The Nineteenth Story

SHAS IBN ZUHAIR AND THE PERFUME SELLER

The Prince of Hira married Miriam, sister of the Fazara leader Hadifa, and the Fazara people claim that the marriage took place in their country; but others say that at this time Aswad went back to Hira for his marriage, and it was the year of the Great Drought. And so it may have been that, as Hadifa travelled on the northern tracks towards Hira, escorting his sister Miriam, he fell in with Shas ibn Zuhair journeying upon the same way and guided by the same Northern Star. Shas was carrying gifts from his noble father to Numan, king of Hira. And the gifts were precious gifts, ambergris purchased from traders in the tropic seas, and yellow amber from the north, sold in Rouad Island and Saida by the Phoenician sailors. Aloes, too, with their bitter juice, and balls of dark musk, and sandalwood from the east for perfume, and citron oils. All these rare gifts were borne by Shas to Hira. And the two men journeyed together, Hadifa with many men, and Shas with but one or two servants.

Now the peace obtaining between the Abs and the Fazara was but a hollow peace, and the malevolence which Aswad felt for 'Antar was intense, and fed upon itself, and it had grown and swollen within Aswad as the thunderclouds may grow and swell and darken the whole bright sky in the rainy season. For he could not forget the humiliation he had suffered at 'Antar's hands. Hadifa also had brooded upon the grievances of Aswad, soon to become his brother-in-law, and he determined to make the journey an unhappy journey for Shas, uncle of

'Antar, and truly he was more successful than he perhaps intended, for at this time, O my listeners, it became clear that even 'Antar himself was subject to the will of the Great Creator, and could not shelter his family and his tribe from misfortune or from the grim reality of fate.

Hadifa, then, as they travelled, spoke ceaselessly in Aswad's praise, and as ceaselessly did he criticize and condemn 'Antar, hero of the Abs people. And at first Shas put up with his companion's chatter, feeling in his heart that 'Antar had indeed been severe in his humiliation of Aswad. Yet, as the hours passed, Shas recollected that Aswad had refused all thought of the reconciliation proffered by 'Antar, which Shas knew to be the nobler way forward. For the great-hearted can admit to faults and can achieve harmony where once was discord, whereas the mean-spirited will foster an injury in the mind and tend it as a vintner tends his wine, till he can crush the last bitter drop from the acid grapes.

So Shas grew impatient with Hadifa, and he cried at last, 'O my companion, let us have an end to this provocation.' But still Hadifa persisted till Shas, weary and furious, halted the whole caravan in the empty desert, just an hour before sunset. 'Enough,' he said, 'I will hear no more, but will travel alone. And should it be, Hadifa, that this senseless teasing has been persisted in especially to taunt me, then you have achieved your object. Yet would I say before I leave you that it was unworthy for an Arab to behave thus, for does not our desert lore teach us that men who are not enemies should travel on the high desert in company, so as to ward off the dangers from which we are seldom free?' Then he turned his camel to the east, and his servants turned theirs in his wake, and he sped across the hard sand in the gathering darkness.

And Hadifa watched him go, ashamed at an accusation which he knew to be true; and uneasy, too, for he felt the premonition of disaster.

Shas and his men became separated in the dusk, but they were unafraid and knew that they could find each other's tracks when the sun rose; so all camped and slept. And Shas in the morning rode to a small oasis where he felt sure his followers would find him. He refreshed his camel and he himself drank at the well, little knowing that this was the last time he would relish the cool, crystal water which the One God gives us as his most precious safeguard against the perils of the desert. For riding towards the oasis was a hunter, Thalaba ibn Aarij, and he had come to claim the beasts which might have entangled themselves in the snares he had set overnight, and the birds from the nets he had spread between poles stuck slantwise into the sand. But as he came near the green bushes and the clear spring water, he saw Shas's camel lumber to its feet, and it strode through both snares and nets, breaking the cords and the poles and destroying the work of many hours' labour by Thalaba and his wife. Rage flooded over Thalaba, and quick as an asp he drew his bow to his shoulder. And a moment later Shas lay dead at the well's edge, the blood running freely from an arrow's wound in his throat, for the hunter in his anger had aimed low, and had struck not the camel but the unseen rider concealed by the green bushes at the waterside.

Now was the hunter aghast at his thoughtless action, and he reproached himself bitterly, entreating Lat and Uzza to restore life to the slain, but alas it was too late, and Thalaba cried, 'Fool that I am to have been so hasty, and more foolish still to have killed a man of power. For here is no ordinary traveller. Had it not been for my anger, which was all the greater since game is so scarce in this year of utter drought, this noble stranger and I had shared a meal together.' And he wept in his sorrow and dismay.

Now all this while a servant of Shas's had observed, in secret, what had passed; but the servant was unarmed, and he had just topped the ridge above the spring as his master fell dying. The servant ran, and summoned his companions, and consulted with them. And Thalaba, too, left the oasis to summon his wife and consult with her, leaving the body of Shas silent and still under the warm wind's caress. And the shadows of the wheeling vultures began to pass and pass again over the oasis.

Thalaba and his wife returned after many days, determined to conceal all that had occurred, so they buried the remains in the soft sand beyond the bushes, and they killed the camel, leaving its body to the vultures' beaks, and they took the camel's saddle with its precious burden of perfumes and wax and yellow amber, and hid these in their own humble tent. And they were of the Aamir people.

So it was that when Shas's servants returned with armed men to avenge Shas's death, there was no trace of his murder; only the bones of a camel glistening white in the sun's glare, and no trace of harness or saddle on the hot sand.

Then came a time of great mourning among the Abs, and Zuhair with Temadhur wept at the loss of their son Shas. And when the days of mourning were fulfilled, the Prince his brother gathered together two thousand men and set off to the Aamir country to avenge the killing; but first they met Gheshm the Spear-thrower, a neighbour of the Aamir. Gheshm heard of the Prince's coming, and rode in to the desert to meet him, for Gheshm knew of no quarrel between the two tribes. And truly the Prince had no belief in violence or warfare, for he had observed as a young man that while these might settle one problem, they could but be followed by a multitude of new dilemmas and difficulties. And the two men met and parted friends, for Gheshm threw doubt upon the whole strange story of Shas's death; and the hunter and his wife had departed long since to a far land.

But Qais, brother of Shas and the Prince, was not satisfied by the Prince's investigations. He loaded two camels with grain, which was in demand, for was this not the year of the Great Drought? And he took with him an old woman who posed as a Yemeni, and she could visit the Aamir women in their tents, and she spoke to them, saying, 'I have good corn to sell, and in return will take anything you can offer, but above all I look for perfumes and scented oils.'

Now after some weeks the old woman, by skilful questioning, found the tent of Thalaba's wife; it was separated from the dwellings of the rest of the tribe by two days' journey, and Thalaba was away among strangers, hoping to sell a camel's saddle, richly decorated, and a camel's bridle, where neither would arouse suspicion. And Thalaba's wife was lonely, and she spoke gladly with the Yemeni woman, offering her musk and ambergris in exchange for the golden grain; and her loneliness rendered her indiscreet, and she revealed in her conversation, yet unknowingly, a clear enough account of her husband's rashness. So did the true story of Shas's death come to be known.

Now that the Abs knew where to lay the blame, they marched against the Beni Aamir, and the two forces met as if to fight — the Abs on the one side and on the other the Beni Ghan, Kilab and Aamir; though the true leader, Khaled ibn Jaafar, was with Prince Aswad in Hira, paying tribute to Numan and dealing with the affairs of his niece Saadia,

141

who was a very troublesome and tiresome girl. But this is another story.

Messengers went between the two forces, and Thalaba was sought yet was not found; but his wife was forced to disclose their treasure, and there was the ambergris and the aloes, the balls of dark musk and the sandalwood and the citron oils arrayed upon rugs spread before her tent, and she wept at this witness to her guilt.

Zuhair's wrath was great, but he believed that the Aamir people had been in ignorance of the crime against the Abs, and when they offered him ten times the usual amount of blood money, he parleyed with their leaders and accepted. But later Rabia influenced them to change their minds, and the Spear-thrower came to help his friends, and battle was joined. And on either side men fought and strove against each other, and this continued for five days.

Yet a peaceful ending was achieved in the sad dispute, as the Prince had wanted. For the sixth day ushered in the month of Rajab, when killings must cease and men should go unarmed, and when wrongs must be righted and forgiven. And Zuhair abandoned his attack so as not to give an evil example. So no further retribution was exacted for the death of Shas.

The Twentieth Story

TRAGEDY IN THE GROVES OF MECCA

The lord Zuhair mourned, then, for his son Shas. But yet further mourning was to be the lot of the Abs, and of 'Antar, the future leader of the tribe, and 'Abla his consort. And this was the way of it. We must recall, O my listeners, the warrior Dhalim ibn Harith of the el Murra tribe, friend of Hadifa who maintained but a hollow peace with his Abs neighbours. Dhalim was he who fought against 'Antar in the valley of Raml. He wielded the great sword Dhu al Hayat, Lord of Life, heirloom of Juban ibn Himyar, King of the Universe; and he was the only warrior ever to break the shaft of 'Antar's spear in combat.

When the year of the Great Drought came to an end, the sons of the lord Zuhair gathered in the Abs camp to see their father and their mother, Temadhur, set off on a pilgrimage to the Sacred Groves of Mecca, thinking to themselves, They will find comfort there for the loss they have suffered in the death of our brother. And indeed the noble pair journeyed slowly, and they took heart as they travelled over the bare desert, greening now under the benison of rain, and they camped for many days in the Valley of the Oak Trees where men come in peace from the sown land to gather rough bark for tanning, and polished acorns for swine food. These men treasure, too, the tiny insects which yield that scarlet dye celebrated by the scribe, he whose uncle perished when the gods poured forth their anger from the fire mountain in Roman lands,

143

when Rome's power was at its height.*

And Zuhair and Temadhur met and parleyed with these men whose lives were so different from their own, and their grief was perhaps somewhat assuaged.

Later they persevered to Mecca, which had long been a centre of peace and veneration since the days when the Friend of God, Abraham, first set foot there (where his footprint is indeed to be seen to this day). But these were unhappy times and the Abs people were to learn that even 'Antar, favourite of their ageing lord, could not shelter them from misfortune or the grim reality of fate. For another pilgrim had come to the Sacred Groves, and this was Khaled ibn Jaafar, returning from Hira where he had travelled to deal with the affairs of his tiresome and troublesome niece — but this is another story. On Khaled's return he heard how his Aamir people had been involved in the murder of Shas, and of the fighting which had followed, and the peace imposed by the advent of Rajab.

So when Zuhair and Khaled met at their devotions, a certain barrier lay between them and they could not easily behave as brothers should in the sacred meadow, for many brave men had perished on both sides, and each leader was unforgiving in his heart.

The two prayed, indeed, at the Ka'aba, but they were disturbed by onlookers who marvelled at the strange flighting of birds overhead, and a newcomer told how he had found similar birds dead upon the ground elsewhere, and rumour grew and spread among the onlookers and they prophesied that doom and death must follow upon these omens. So Khaled and Zuhair became even more uneasy and restive, and neither found peace in his prayer or meditation.

Now it happened that when Zuhair had first come to Mecca as a young man, before his marriage, he had been enchanted by the healing qualities of the valley and moved by its power for good, and he had returned to his people and in the mejlis he had cried, 'O my people, truly in Mecca is great devotion, and sustenance for us all. Let us now establish a similar altar here in our own country where men may find security and peace.' For he was but a young man and did not appreciate that the holiness of Mecca came from the One Lord through

*The reference to the uncle and the scribe is to the elder and the younger Pliny. The oak is *Quercus coccifera*.

144

his Friend, Abraham. And an ancient sheikh arose in the assembly and spoke fearlessly to Zuhair, saying, 'O my lord, this cannot be done; for most certainly it would be a criminal thing to imitate the Ka'aba, mansion of the blessed Abraham, and assuredly punishment would fall upon us all for our temerity were we to do as you suggest.' And Zuhair learned of the old man, and he bore the rebuke with humility, saying, 'Indeed you are right, my friend, and I was wrong and thoughtless. This was the idea of a man uninstructed in religious matters.'

Yet had this story lived, and now Khaled spoke of it to Zuhair, and Zuhair was greatly affronted to have his youthful folly recalled in such surroundings; and, moreover, as passions were aroused between the two leaders, so memories of the past conflict fanned the flames. Dark birds flocked over the Ka'aba, and Zuhair, in the madness of rage, flung insult after insult at his adversary, and threatened him with violence and destruction. Only his close companions held him, otherwise might he have profaned that sacred place with blood.

And the onlookers murmured among themselves, saying, 'Here was a noble leader, but alas he has given way to wickedness and will surely have to expiate his evil in one way or another.' And one by one they turned from the two angry men and their companions, deeply moved by the baleful and injurious tragedy being enacted under a darkening sky.

The companions of the two men were successful in averting the shame of an encounter in the very shadow of the Ka'aba, and Khaled departed with his followers and returned home; whereas Zuhair, deeply troubled, sought out the assembly at Ukadh, hoping to soothe his grief and anger with the healing essence of poetry. But he could find no peace. He, too, departed, and set up camp at Howazin.

Now Qais, brother of Shas, feared that his father's authority was waning and that his judgement was less sound than in earlier days, and he heard, too, that Khaled had been angered by some great trouble at Mecca. And he set off with armed men to join his father at Howazin.

It had happened long before that one of Temadhur's brothers, Amr by name, had offended the Abs people and been banished, and he had sought shelter with the Aamir. And now Khaled summoned him, saying, 'For many years you have enjoyed our hospitality, O Amr ibn Shedid, and now can you repay us. Go then and seek your sister Temadhur to congratulate her on her pilgrimage to the Mecca shrine, and while you are with her, spy out the land for me and instruct me where I may lie in wait for Zuhair and fight him, for truly he has behaved in an abominable manner and honour must be avenged.' Now Amr was a weak man, but he loved his sister from whom he had been parted so many years. He had no choice but to fall in with his overlord's plans, yet did he fear for Temadhur, and he made a pact with Khaled, saying: 'O my lord, it is evident that you have been insulted by Zuhair, as indeed have I been myself, for was I not banished from among his people? Yet would I not injure my sister, or her sons. And so, O Khaled, may we swear an oath that if I should take part in this plot against our mutual enemy, who, to my mind, fully deserves death, Temadhur must remain a free woman and her sons must live?' And so an oath was sworn, for is it not part of the Arab way that a member of the tribe, however humble, can speak on equal terms with his lord?

When Qais therefore came to Howazin, uneasy and disturbed as he already was, he found Amr there also, and this increased his anxiety. Amr sought out his sister and wished her well, but he hated Zuhair in his heart, and all the while his quick eyes flickered over the camp, and the men and their horses and arms, like a serpent's tongue. And Temadhur welcomed her brother, but Zuhair rebuffed him, saying, 'Begone, Amr ibn Amr ibn Shedid, for I trust you not, nor he who may well have sent you here.' And Qais seized Amr when he had ridden but an hour from the camp, and at the dagger's point made Amr swear to give no information to the lord Khaled.

Then Temadhur reproached Qais for his lack of courtesy, and Zuhair reproached him for his cowardice, saying, 'My son, we need not fear the Aamir people.' But Qais felt dread in his heart and dared not answer either of his parents.

Three days later dust was seen upon the horizon, and Qais wept at the sight of it, for arrayed against the Absians, who numbered but a hundred men, was a force of five thousand — the Aamir, and Rabia ibn Ocail and Sawda ibn Bekr and many more. Khaled rode out from the host, challenging Zuhair to fight with him, and the two lords clashed in combat. But alas for the Abs, and all who owed them allegiance, the threats and insults which Zuhair had hurled so inopportunely at his opponent undermined his strength, for there was no justice in his cause save in the murder of his son Shas.

And in front of the two armies Khaled unhorsed Zuhair in vengeance for the arrogant speeches at Mecca, and as Zuhair lay helpless, Warca, his friend, ran to defend him. But Jandah the Aamiri struck a mortal blow. And the old lord lay dead at last — loved, feared and honoured by many, and betrayed by his own actions in the end. Then was his sword, Zinoor, taken by Khaled, and Khaled rode Zuhair's horse, Qa'asa.

Dumbfounded, Temadhur and her men had no more stomach for the fight, and they were taken; though in honour of the oath sworn between Khaled and Amr no lives were spent; and the Abs people mourned their lord and were allowed to bury him there at the desert's edge, near Howazin. Warca cursed himself for failing in his leader's defence, and Temadhur grieved, and thought at first to follow her lord by her own hand; yet did her good sense prevail and she said to herself, 'Nay, though my heart yearns after him, still I have much to accomplish for my people.' And the tiny band of Absians were allowed to pass through the Aamir lines and to regain home; even Qais being protected by the oath between Khaled and Amr.

Only Gheshm the Spear-thrower rose in anger and reproached Khaled for sparing Zuhair's sons, yet Khaled said, 'I do not fear his sons, rather do I fear the new leader of the tribe, who will assuredly be 'Antar, the warrior poet. For we have cut off the serpent's head, but the tail remains.' But Gheshm thought of 'Antar, for all his gallantry and skill, as a slave, unworthy of succession in the tribe.

Now 'Antar was in a far country, but returning to the west after the adventurous expedition to the fire mountain, and he knew nothing of Khaled's victory, nor did he know that Khaled had ridden east to meet him and lay in ambush among the low hills rising to the High Yemen. And 'Antar's forces were surprised, and a great battle took place, but 'Antar proved a more formidable leader than the ageing sheikh, and his strength prevailed so that Khaled's main force fled to the wind's end. And Khaled, seeing himself almost deserted, rode up to 'Antar on Zuhair's horse Qa'asa, bearing Zuhair's sword Zinoor, and he cried, 'O 'Antar, your noble uncle has but recently given me his horse and his own sword since we have agreed to forget the quarrel which cleaves between my people and your own like a chasm in the Yemeni mountains from which you have come to this battle. Let us also have peace between us. Never would I have attacked had I known your true identity, for I was journeying in peace to the mountain country to barter for jewels with scarlet cloth dyed in the Valley of the Oaks.'

And 'Antar was deceived, for his noble mind could not grasp the depth of Khaled's deception; and 'Antar felt ashamed, and he released his prisoners, continuing on his way.

So he came to Mount Saadi, and his homeland of Shereba, and as he rode he heard the sound of lamentation borne on the western breeze, and his pace quickened, and with his men behind him he galloped into the camp with trepidation in his heart.

Then Shiboob, who was among the fighters, remembered that day so long ago when, believing 'Antar dead, he had found the camp in mourning for them both, for it had been sundown, then as now, and he had seen the women of the tribe busy at their cooking pots and bread ovens, and the smoke from a hundred fires rising in the still air. And smoke from the burning camel dung brought tears to his eyes, but the eyes of those in the camp were already red with weeping, as his own had been so long ago.

'Antar too could sense some great disaster, and he spurred Abjer on to meet the Prince, who rode towards them, weeping and alone. And the Prince cried to his friend, 'O 'Antar, prepare yourself for grievous news, for Zuhair is dead — our lord and noble leader is dead.'

And 'Antar gave a great shout and fell senseless at the Prince's feet, and it was as though a tremor had shivered down the Jordan valley, bringing the churches of high Jerusalem to ruins. But when strength returned he remounted and with the Prince rode to meet Qais, weeping also and alone; and though 'Antar's heart was weighed down with grief, he slipped from Abjer's saddle and vowed allegiance. And together they rode in to a sad welcome from the sorrowing men and women of the encampment.

REVENGE AND THE RISING DARK SHADOW OF HARITH IBN DHALIM

'My hopes lay in thy hands,

O my lord, my friend.

My grief and my despair lay like a cloak about
thy shoulders,

O my lord, my friend.

From thy hands have I received protection,
Magnanimity didst thou wear, and comfort, like a garment,
Like a cloak about thy shoulders,

O my lord, my friend.

I have been overwhelmed by the generous bounty of thy
great heart,
Now it is pierced, and empty,

O my friend, my lord,

No more may I depend upon thee, thou who hast saved me
From death and catastrophe.'

So sang 'Antar over the death of his lord, Zuhair, and all
mourned with him, and with grief came anger as 'Antar
learned from the Prince how Khaled had fought with Zuhair
and how Jandah had struck the final blow. And 'Antar's anger
increased when he realized how Khaled, riding upon Zuhair's
own horse and wielding Zuhair's own sword, had most

dishonourably tricked him into avoiding a fight over the fallen leader.

Now Qais took the leadership upon himself, and because of 'Antar's open display of loyalty there was no faction supporting the claims of the younger man. Yet was division to spread within the tribe as an unseen corruption may moulder within a warm apricot until the sweet fruit is rotten and brown stains disfigure the orange velvet of its skin. The corruption, men say, spread from the heart of Harith ibn Dhalim, the evil one, the Impostor; for here was a treacherous man and strong, one who regarded no hospitality, who respected no promise. And Harith hated 'Antar, who had so savagely shamed his father at the battle of the pools of Akhrem.

Qais then sent out his messengers to the tribes, Fazara, Ghitafan and Dhibyan and many more, demanding help in avenging his father's death; and Qais recalled Rabia at this time to assist the Abs people. Rabia, however, put his hatred of 'Antar above any other loyalty, and he persuaded Qais that Harith should fight for him, if he would agree, for Harith would be a stronger arm in battle even than 'Antar. So Qais sent messages to Harith by way of Hadifa, then sent out his own heralds to bring in fighting men for the tasks ahead, and among those he summoned was Harith ibn Dhalim of the Murra; for Hadifa was willing to support Qais in this blood feud with the Aamir as he could see in Harith a rival to 'Antar, and he hoped to win advantage from division within the Abs since at this time the peace between Abs and Fazara was but a hollow peace.

So it happened that at the same time Harith ibn Dhalim received messages from Khaled asking for support, and reminding him of 'Antar's crimes against his father; and also from Qais by way of Rabia, and from Hadifa. And Khaled offered Harith marriage terms with his own daughter. So Harith agreed to serve Khaled, yet did he tell the messengers from Hadifa that he would fight on Qais's side, for here was a man who saw no value in truth. Hadifa assured Qais that help would come from the Marra men, and the forces set off from all sides across the desert to meet and battle over the death of the lord Zuhair. Yet did the Prince advise 'Antar to remain in the camp for a time, knowing that Rabia and Amara had had dealings with Harith and wishing to protect 'Antar from any injury until he was convinced of Harith's good faith. For the good and noble souls on this earth can sense evil in other men as a horse may sense the presence of a hyena hidden among the rocks and refuse to go further.

But, half-way to Khaled's territories, Qais and his forces were halted by men of Harith ibn Dhalim's, marshalled in the desert across the tracks leading to the east, and the two armies came face to face. And some of these men of Harith's were Beni Aamir; and Harith rode upon Zuhair's horse, and he wielded Zuhair's sword.

Hadifa then rode forward and cried to Harith ibn Dhalim, 'O Harith, I had thought you were my friend, yet here you are opposing me with your sword, and your men arrayed behind you as if for battle. Are you then friend or foe?' And Harith answered, laughing, 'Your friendship is nothing to me, we meet as enemies.' And he taunted Hadifa with his own simplicity and spurred against him with all the advantage which hypocrisy can bestow upon an evil man in battle against those who believe in the higher good: and the two men clashed.

Things went cruelly for Hadifa, and at length he was delivered from death only by the services of his faithful brother, Haml, and as darkness fell the Abs and the Fazara men were dismayed by this unexpected attack; and Rabia repented of his hopes for 'Antar's discomfiture and confessed these hopes to Qais. And all the leaders joined in urgent plans to seek for reinforcements, either from Numan or from 'Antar himself. And while Amara spoke up against summoning 'Antar, he was silenced by Asyed, who said, 'Nay, Amara, your private dislikes must not enter into this, for the very welfare of our people is at stake, and as the proverb has it, "While the remedy is on its way from 'Iraq, he who is bitten by the viper may well die." ' So horsemen were sent to fetch 'Antar.

But 'Antar had fretted in the camp after all his fighting companions had left, and he began to feel that the Prince had been wrong in counselling delay. Yet had 'Antar few horses or men at his disposal. So he had to avail himself of packhorses; and he and his friends and brothers disguised themselves as a knight in black armour with a band of followers, and they set off to join not their friends but their foes — the Aamir. 'For,' said 'Antar, 'Harith ibn Dhalim, the Impostor, is fighting for Qais, and we must oppose Harith even if it means deceiving our dear friends who are most assuredly in danger when they avail themselves of his services.' They journeyed for two days to the field of battle, and merged themselves with the Aamir forces in the confusion and the dust and the darkness after the first day of the fighting.

When, therefore, Hadifa was wounded, they saw him fall; and they saw by whom he was attacked; and they saw also Nazih, young and beloved son of Asyed, the brother of Zuhair, ride furiously to the van of the two armies, challenging Harith to defend himself and his dishonour. And Asyed watched, fearing for his son's safety.

But as the two warriors wheeled to the fight, a Black Knight burst forth from the Aamir vanguard, crying, 'Nay, Harith ibn Dhalim, you have fought long enough and engage too young an opponent. Lay up your arms, now, or use them against me in single combat.' And all were amazed, for though the knight's armour was finely wrought, yet his horse was but a packhorse and his lance was short and brittle, and indeed, in the first clash it was broken into four pieces by Harith ibn Dhalim. And Harith thought to himself, Just so did my father break 'Antar's spear before his humiliation. Should not my father's son pit himself against a more worthy opponent than this rustic here? And he smiled to himself as the Black Knight spliced the short haft with cord. But Nazih offered the knight his own horse and his own strong spear, sensing something unusual in the older man's strange and sudden appearance.

Then the two clashed again, and there was no more laughter and no more sneering at the Black Knight, for his blow unhorsed Harith, who lay helpless, awaiting death. Yet did the knight ignore him, and strangely did capture the runaway horse and retrieve the abandoned sword, and these he handed to Nazih with a silent bow. And Nazih rode back to his father and his uncles, and a great discussion arose among them as he came, and Qais cried, 'O my companions, what is this we see! Who is this Black Knight who has unhorsed our treacherous enemy, is it indeed 'Antar?' 'How could this be,' answered Sheddad, 'when our messengers left for the camp only a few hours ago? Yet indeed, cousin, the knight's movements are strangely like those of my noble son.' And moreover the horse he has delivered to Nazih is no other than Qa'asa, and the sword no other than Zinoor — the steed and the weapon of our dead lord.' 'Can it be,' cried Qais, 'that, hearing me accept Rabia's judgement that Harith would prove a more valued ally, 'Antar has crept in among us to confuse us all?'

152

And so it proved. And 'Antar's friends watched him as, one by one, he challenged and threw all those who had been involved in Shas's death and in Zuhair's death, saving only Khaled himself, and Harith who was now a prisoner among the Abs. And among those he captured was Jandah who had struck the final blow which killed Zuhair. And all could see that 'Antar had wrought well in avenging his lord, and indeed, had 'Antar not persuaded him, Nazih himself would never have come to battle under Qais's leadership, for the corruption of men such as Harith ibn Dhalim and Rabia had already worked upon the inner unity of the tribe, and secret whispering had already corrupted loyalty.

Yet at this time 'Antar's actions in the guise of the Black Knight precluded further bloodshed, for the main force of Khaled's men, advancing, withdrew to their inner fastness, brooding over the fate of Harith, now a prisoner, and of Jandah, who had been judged and decapitated by Qais with his father's sword.

And as for Harith ibn Dhalim, he was brought in chains to the mejlis for judgement, and his treachery was laid bare before everyone. Yet did he plead he had done all this simply to challenge 'Antar, and that he would now in his humiliation acknowledge his faults and ask pardon. Then Rabia advised his release, for he hoped Harith ibn Dhalim would again attack 'Antar; and Sheddad advised death, for he feared the evil he could not understand. But 'Antar himself pressed Harith, saying, 'O Harith, I have heard much of your perfidy, yet would I not pass judgement of death upon a clever fighter.' And Harith answered, ' 'Antar, the lesson has been well learnt, and I am a changed man if you would but believe it.' And 'Antar's nobility precluded the doubting of such a statement, so convincing was the ring of truth in Harith's voice. And 'Antar cried, rejoicing, 'Harith, I humiliated your father perhaps too harshly, and he died unable to accept my offer to discuss and rectify the matter between us, as men of honour may do. Now let there be peace between you and me.' And Harith agreed that this should be so, but he was insincere, and he hated 'Antar all the more for his own defeat. But 'Antar believed him; and being in merry mood for the first time since Zuhair's death, he freed Harith and sent him to rejoin Rabia, who stood surety for his good behaviour.

But later in the darkness of the night, Rabia questioned his friend, saying, 'What am I to believe, Harith? Have you exchanged the lonely path of vengeance and destruction for the road of righteousness?' And Harith ibn Dhalim laughed, as he had laughed at Hadifa's innocent trust, and he whispered, 'Nay, my friend, my path lies towards vengeance and destruction still; and it is a dark path and a lonely path as you have hinted. For in opposing 'Antar I have only a few companions.'

The Twenty-second Story

'ANTAR A CAPTIVE OF THE KHULAN WOMEN

Now for many months an uneasy and fragile truce was maintained among the tribes, but ever the bitterness between Abs and Zaiyad increased, for Rabia and the jealous Amara could never accept the advent of 'Antar into their lives and their councils as an equal. Even though 'Antar had saved Amara's life in fighting with Khaled's men before the truce was established, Amara still plotted against his cousin, and Qais was greatly worried by the continued enmity which even a noble action could not heal. And he rebuked Amara before all the tribe, but nothing could change him. Then, fearing Qais's displeasure, Amara and Rabia journeyed away to Yamouriyah because of the truce which was to ensure a year's abstinence from fighting between the Abs and the Aamir.

But Qais began to hear rumours of war. The Beni Aamir were, in spite of the truce, preparing again for battle; and Khaled was sending out messengers on all sides to gather both weapons and men, truce or no truce. He had already welcomed Dhuraid ibn Samah, of Howazin and Jeshan and Hamadan; and Dhuraid was 450 years of age; and the millstone of war seemed once more to be threatening to crush them all. So Qais, worried and anxious as was his temperament, left also with a few men for Yamouriyah to seek arms and reinforcements, and to find messengers among the Zaiyad. And he came to Yamouriyah, and there a most comical adventure befell him, and this was the way of it.

155

Qais had passed through Medina Yathreb, and there he met his old friend Ajija ibn Jella, he who was related to Abd al Muttalib by blood on his mother's side. And Ajija was possessed of a most marvellous coat of mail, intricately woven and of great strength and beauty. And Qais coveted this coat and asked if he might purchase it, but Ajija said, 'Alas, my old friend, Khaled, your enemy, has already requested it, flattering me withal by praising my poetry, and I am in no position to ignore his demand.' So the two men spoke of other things, agreeing over the coffee cups on the number of swords and lances which could be spared to Qais should Khaled attack. But later, as the two friends drank wine together, for this was in the time of Ignorance, Ajija said: 'In sooth I have a mind to ignore Khaled's request, despite his praise for my poems: bid, then, for the coat of mail, my friend, and let us bargain as true companions should!' And Qais, who could truly assess Ajija's generosity, bid but a hundred camels, and Ajija would accept but one, for is it not the Arab way to give his guests anything they may admire? So Qais continued to Yamouriyah with his marvellous coat, and his slaves returned to the Abs, bearing weapons and promises of men to wield them.

Now when Rabia saw the intricate coat of mail his whole being craved for its possession, and he spoke to Qais, saying, 'My lord, let me put it on so you may see what a brave sight it makes of a man.' And Qais agreed, smiling, because the mail coat hung about Rabia's heels like a woman's robe, though he was not a short man. Yet was Qais's smile turned instantly to anger and dismay, for Rabia rushed from the tent, returning, sword in hand, to accuse Qais of theft. And Qais was stupefied by the arrogance and impertinence of Rabia, and a violent quarrel took place; but Qais could do nothing, for he was unarmed and had only a few slaves with him.

Then did Rabia and the Zaiyad company mock him, and they called out insolently, 'O Qais, see, you have lost your dear possession which should have protected any man. We have outwitted you, yet will we return the coat in exchange for 'Antar should he come alone unarmed!' And in truth there was a threat concealed in their insolence, like a dagger concealed in a silken sleeve. Yet was Qais to be aided by his womenfolk, for on the following day there came his wife and her servants to seek him, and with them was his daughter Jemana, who was as famous for her wit and wisdom as for her skill at poetry. She could weave words and verses of magic meaning, and her poems were as delightful as pearls upon a thread.

Her father said, 'O Jemana, help me with your wisdom, for truly I have been tricked as easily as a small boy of less than seven years, and if this story goes about, all Arabs will accuse me of imbecility.' And Jemana approached Rabia, yet for all her skills as advocate and poet he would not yield, saying only, 'Yes, when I have fought against Khaled in this mail shirt, then I may return it, but not till then.' So Jemana bided her time, and she sent for 'Antar to help her; but meanwhile she persuaded Qais to pretend acquiescence so as to save his face, and so as to preserve what unity he could between the Abs and the Zaiyad.

On receiving Jemana's message, Shiboob and 'Antar advanced in secret upon the Zaiyad in Yamouriyah, but before they left camp they surprised Amara, who had returned there and who was spying, in a slave's disguise, upon 'Abla's privacy. And he was taken out and beaten mercilessly by Shiboob, and had indeed to spend many days recovering in the tent of Zebeeba, mother of 'Antar, before he dared appear before the tribe. So Shiboob and 'Antar rode in a mood of great anger to Yamouriyah, and there 'Antar challenged Rabia for the coat of mail.

Now the Prince had heard of Amara's unpardonable attempts to invade 'Abla's privacy, and he had advised 'Antar to kill Amara. And this advice had great influence with 'Antar, for the Prince dealt only in justice and had little faith in violence. Yet 'Antar had stayed his hand; and again, when he unhorsed Rabia, battling for the coat of mail, and when Rabia lay helpless before him, and even as he raised his black sword Dami, 'Antar knew within himself that he must not use it. He turned in disgust from his cousin, saying, 'Leave, then, the silver coat upon the sand. It is the lord's.' And Rabia complied, and fled in shame and fear.

And now, O my listeners, we come at last to the story of how 'Antar was held captive by the women of the Khulan tribe, and it happened thus, and Rabia's knavery was at the bottom of it:

Qais sent for 'Antar to consult with him on the matter of Khaled's threats, but none could find him and 'Abla said, 'O my lord Qais, a crier cried for him in the night, and he was gone.'

Then a great fear settled upon them all, for many men were

advancing against them and the nervous temperament of Qais infected all of them with doubt, and their spirits ebbed from them. Then came Rabia, riding fast to the camp and announcing that he had killed 'Antar in battle; and indeed he believed 'Antar to be dead, though the news itself was false news. Yet, while the Abs people stood stunned by the shock of his proclamation, Rabia leapt again to his horse and raced Qais's messengers to Hadifa. 'Send no help to Qais,' he advised. ' 'Antar is dead, and nothing remains for them but defeat.' Yet did he join with the Fazara people in skirmishing against Dhuraid's brother Abdalla and his men, though the main burden of the fighting lay upon the Abs, and truly the millstone of war weighed heavily upon them all. For three days the battle raged, and on the fourth day Sheddad, the old warrior, bowed down with grief at his son's supposed death, was captured; and Urwah too was made a prisoner, and the cold hand of despair clutched at the heart of Qais as he rallied his men in the noonday heat. As he led them into the thick of the fray, he hurled his helmet from him, believing that all hope was lost and that death would claim them all.

Yet at this very moment a cloud of dust arose on the eastern plain, and the Beni Aamir wheeled to face a foe who could not be defeated, for 'Antar himself led innumerable horsemen to the battle, and the Abs were saved. Khaled and Dhuraid and their men fled as chaff before the wind, and Rabia and Amara fled too, with Harith, to a secret valley, amazed and angry, for they had believed 'Antar to be truly dead.

They had indeed plotted his capture with ingenuity, lying in wait for him in a secret place with a band of slaves, and one night a slave had been sent to fetch 'Antar, pretending that some chivalrous enterprise was afoot, and so 'Antar, riding Abjer, and Shiboob with him, rode out at dead of night. This slave was the crier who cried for him, as 'Abla had told Qais.

Both 'Antar and Shiboob were wary of the slave and his mission, but in chivalry no questioning is possible since prudence may denote fear, which no knight can admit to. As the poet says:

> They will arise when they are called
>   By one who is afraid,
> They are away, unquestioning they ride

158

To succour those who are afraid.
They will return in honour to their friends.

So, through 'Antar's honour, Rabia effected his capture, though 'Antar had the satisfaction of killing the false slave before he himself was overpowered and bound. Yet even so this only occurred because, in that narrow valley, 'Antar and Shiboob could discover no path of escape for the horses. And they were taken and bound, each upon his own steed, and led down the steep defile to the desert floor where Rabia and Amara waited to mock them. But then, as Amara advanced to kill his hated cousin and rival, the thunder of hoofs was heard and dust arose, and a troop of five hundred raiders advanced at such speed in the early sunshine of the morning that Amara had no time to think of anything but his own safety.

In the confusion, 'Antar and Shiboob were saved by the sagacity of Abjer, for he had been trained always to speed towards the attacking forces and never to fly from them; so he galloped like the wind itself towards the raiders, and Shiboob's horse followed, and the prisoners, though still bound, at least exchanged the immediate prospect of death for the lighter burden of renewed captivity.

Now the raiding party was led by Mushajaa ibn Husan of the Khulan, who owed allegiance to the lord Safwan. And Mushajaa knew that 'Antar had fought against his lord, and he led 'Antar and Shiboob to his own camp. But Rabia and Amara fled, all their slaves being killed, and they thought 'Antar and Shiboob had died also at the raiders' hands.

Now 'Antar and Shiboob were later brought to Safwan, but before any judgement could be passed upon them an old woman rose up in the crowd, crying, 'O Safwan, and you my lord Mushajaa, this man may have fought against our tribe, yet this is but the way of the desert rulers and the riders of death, and he has done such noble deeds that he must be spared. For he is no other than 'Antar ibn Sheddad who once overwhelmed my own son with his generosity.' And all were astonished to hear from the old woman how her son had once taken a thousand of 'Antar's camels, and how 'Antar had recaptured them; but had then, on hearing they were for a dowry, released the boy raider and the camels, and had more-over added a further three hundred to the flock. So 'Antar and Shiboob were relieved of all but their wrist bonds, and were treated with some kindness by the Khulan women.

Next day the tribe was attacked, and the men rode off to defend the camp; but things went badly for them and the women feared defeat. Then the old woman spoke up, saying, 'My sisters, we have a sure means of defence here among us. Let us ask 'Antar and his brother to fight for us, for are we not confident of the nobility of his character? I for one do not believe he would harm any one of us, or despoil our property.' And after long discussion, the women came to 'Antar with this proposition, adding, 'Indeed, sir, we trust you both and would welcome your help against the enemy, yet can we see that our menfolk might well berate us for the risk we take, and might even perhaps be unable to accept the aid you could render them, so foolish are men when it comes to matters of this kind. Would you agree, O noble warriors, to resume your fetters once the battle is won?'

Then 'Antar and Shiboob laughed together, and they agreed to this endearing request; and together they diverted the enemy from the main battle, and led them away and defeated them, yet still returned to the camp before the Khulan men rode home, sorely battered in an unequal fight.

And on their return the two gallant prisoners were found bound and helpless as in the morning; yet were their horses drenched in sweat, and such merriment and gay familiarity passed between the prisoners and the Khulan women that the day's adventures could not be concealed. So all ended in feasting and jollity, with Mushajaa entertaining his prisoners as guests and loading them with presents in gratitude for the part they had played in the fight, and for the nobility with which they had kept their strange promise to the Khulan women in resuming their fetters.

On the following day 'Antar and Shiboob were allowed to leave the Beni Khulan, and they set off for home, and as they rode, still laughing at their adventures, they came across a band of shepherds who told of a great battle between the Abs and the Aamir and other tribes.

Then did 'Antar and Shiboob round up what friends they could muster, and they rode fast to the fighting, and the Aamir army, in the moment of their triumph, were overwhelmed when they wheeled to face a foe who could not be defeated. They fled as chaff is blown before the wind. And their prisoners were freed.

But 'Antar and Shiboob were welcomed as ones who had returned from the dead, and Qais ordered celebrations and feasting for many days, so great was his joy in the return of 'Antar from his ordeal at the hands of Rabia, and from his more enjoyable captivity among the Khulan women.

The Twenty-third Story

THE TRAGEDY OF HARITH'S KILLINGS

The enemies of 'Antar are remembered: Hijar and Dhalim, whom he humiliated in the battle of the pools of Akhrem; Maadi Kereb (who was yet to become his friend); and Dhuraid, who was over four hundred years old and yet survived to the time of the Prophet — upon whom be peace. Among these enemies some, like Maadi Kereb, became friends since they could recognize the noble attributes of their foe and learn to respect him. But Dhalim died in bitterness, and his son, Harith the Impostor, bore upon strong and willing shoulders the mantle of hatred inherited from his father; and he became a corrupt and treacherous man who regarded not the rules of hospitality, and who held even the most solemn oath or promise in disrespect.

When 'Antar rescued his tribe from the wrath of the Aamir, and sent their fighting men flying for shelter in 'Iraq, like sparks carried before the wind, Harith's hatred was enhanced by bitter envy at 'Antar's success, and by his unmatched nobility. And Harith fled, though he, too, had been skirmishing against Khaled's army. And he headed north across the desert, to 'Iraq, by a different way.

So it came about that Harith ibn Dhalim rode into Hira at about the same time as Khaled and his men found shelter there. Khaled was a guest in the court of King Numan; but Harith was a guest in the tents of his sister Selma, wife of Sinan ibn abi Haritha; and she was wet-nurse to the children of the King Numan by his first wife now dead. As Harith rode to her tents, Selma was nursing the king's infant son, Shirjibeel, and Harith's dark shadow fell across the boy's face so that Selma looked up in alarm; yet then she recognized her brother. And Shirjibeel was a lovely child.

Now King Numan was bound in marriage, O my listeners, to Mutajerida, daughter of King Zuhair. When first he heard of the trials of the Abs and Fazara tribes in their struggle against Khaled, he had been moved to come to their aid. But before he could send reinforcements the defeated Aamir men came to him for shelter, and King Numan said to Mutajerida, 'This unfruitful war will be of no advantage to my liege Chosroes, and is unpleasing also to me; let us hear Khaled's version of its causes, so maybe we shall find a way towards peace, as a man may peer at the sharp sand and the soft sand, seeking the trail of his hunted quarry.' And Mutajerida agreed. So Khaled was summoned before them, before Numan and before Mutajerida, whose brother and whose father had been slain by the Aamir. But Khaled knew no fear, and he spoke out bravely, crying, 'O king, and you Mutajerida, daughter of the lord Zuhair, know you that the death of Shas was accomplished without my knowledge. It was by chance, and I and my people were in no way to blame. Nevertheless, Zuhair would make no allowance for the ways of fate with which we are all familiar, and through his implacable behaviour, which betrayed all the magnanimity of this great-hearted man, he brought his death upon himself. So does he leave me doubly aggrieved, for had he parleyed with me as an equal he would have been alive to this day, and the matter of his son's death could well have been avenged without the slaughter of those twelve hundred men and more for which Qais is now responsible. And I would say now before witnesses that I see no glory in pursuing this path of blood and sorrow, rather would I arrange a peace between us and offer good terms for every death that has occurred.' Now Khaled persuaded some of Numan's court, and Prince Aswad especially pitied him and pleaded for him to Numan. And the idea of a truce was accepted by Numan and by Khaled.

Mutajerida, too, could see that Khaled had pleaded a fair case, and although her heart yearned for her brother Shas and for her father, she knew that Shas had been a victim of the gods' caprice, and she feared that Zuhair had indeed lost some measure of his wisdom and judgement in his latter days. So she supported the idea of a peace between the Abs and the Aamir, and like many women before her time and after, she saw but little sense in the continuance of fighting. She had often argued with her husband upon this matter, laughing and saying to him, 'O my lord, should a division arise between us, I should assuredly have justice upon my side, yet should we bring our quarrel to the test of arms, you would assuredly win, for I am no Robab! How then can I take these expeditions of yours seriously? For where injustice festers there will be sickness, and no skill in arms can heal it.' And Numan would answer, 'Nay, my love, a man must not only die but kill for his true belief; it is his fate. And moreover,' he would add, 'you have other and more deadly weapons in common with all womankind, not excluding Robab.' And the two would spend their days and nights in peace and in merriment, unable to imagine any division between them, so great was their love.

Now Numan ordered that a feast be set before Khaled and his Aamir people. Yet was this brave justification the last of Khaled's actions upon this earth, and the rich feast was the last that he should eat, and the glowing wine the last he should drink; for a bitter madness spread in the brain of Harith ibn Dhalim as he saw not only glory and honour in store for his hated enemy, 'Antar, from the battles recently won, but peace also, and prosperity as a result of this unusual and most sensible truce.

And Harith crept into Khaled's tent in the dark, and cleft Khaled's head from his body with one close stroke of his father's sword, Dhu al Hayat. And he waited there, tense and silent in the darkness, peering at the severed head; and later in his madness he stabbed the still body with his dagger, but now no blood would run.

Then he fled distraught from the dark tents, and stumbled over the fields by the city's western gates, far beyond his sister's dwelling, and he hid himself in the dunes on the desert's edge. And at daybreak the cry of mourning came to him over the dew-drenched fields, and he could see the townsmen and women clustering at the gate, demanding news and questioning each other. 'Who could have done this terrible thing?' they said. 'Assuredly we owed the victim protection as a fugitive, and neither Numan nor Chosroes will find any pleasure in this secret killing.'

Now Khaled's brother had discovered the murder in the

early hours of the dawn, and he roused the Prince Aswad, and an order was issued that Numan's men should surround and question all strangers in the city. So Harith saw his own few followers arrested and questioned in the fields between the city gate and the dunes, and his madness spurred him towards them unknowing, and he shouted, 'This death is my doing, for good or ill I know not!' And he laid about him with Dhu al Hayat, wounding both friend and foe. Then he seized a horse and fled, laughing and crying, to the desert; and his men and the men of Hira could see he was possessed, and they dared not follow.

Yet, when darkness fell, sorrow and repentance overtook him, and leading his horse he crept back to the tents outside the city, and he took refuge with his sister, whispering to her, 'Alas, Selma, I have killed Khaled, leader of the Aamir people, while he was under the protection of King Numan. Yet fear not, for I was drunk with wine and will harm no one else.' And she brought him into her own tent, and as he passed before the gleaming lamp his dark shadow swung across the face of the infant Shirjibeel, asleep upon the cushions.

When dawn broke, Selma brought food to Harith, and milk to drink, and she carried with her the young child, and her heart was full of pity for her brother, who cowered now like a strange dog in the shadow of the tent, and she cried, 'Nay, Harith, refresh yourself and come outside to greet the morning, it is not good to suffer in the dark' — and he came out like a blind man. But when his eyes narrowed to the light he saw men advancing with swords and staves, and behind them a rabble at the city gate, half-fearful, half-curious; and despair settled upon him, for he thought, They do not understand. If then my crime is worse than the crimes of other men in battle, if I am to be treated as a common murderer rather than as a hero, let them all see the depths of my malignity.

And he seized Shirjibeel from his sister and tossed him high, and as the boy fell he was pierced by Harith's deadly sword. And he was a lovely child.

All the men advancing, and all the crowds by the city gate and Selma herself, were struck dumb; and they retreated in fear as if from a serpent. Then Selma alone began to weep over the dead infant, and when she raised her head Harith was gone and his horse with him.

At noonday the stupor which had paralysed the people of

Hira was lifted from them, and mounting anger and disgust impelled the warriors who rode through the western gate and traced Harith and his horse to the desert's edge, and there they found him crazed and shouting among the rocks of the escarpment, and he fought with the strength of ten men, defending the path to his stronghold and killing every man who attempted to climb it. And as the sun sank behind him, he ran to the hilltop and raised his sword Dhu al Hayat and with a shout brought it smashing down upon the rocks — but the rock itself split open, and none dared advance upon him in the gathering darkness.

So the men of Hira consulted together and agreed among themselves to lie to Numan. 'Harith has escaped,' they said. 'He fled straight into the desert and we had no chance to apprehend him.'

But later, when Harith had in reality fled to the desert, Numan ascertained their deception, and grief-stricken and enraged as he was over the death of his child, he summoned Selma and her husband Sinan and bade them, who shared his sorrow and his anger, to seek out the truth. And it became known that Harith had fled westwards, but yet later northwards over the two rivers to the high mountains. But none dared to follow.

And to this day mothers will say with a shudder to their children, 'Nay, my children, do not quarrel thus. Else will each among you become like Harith ibn Dhalim, he who slaughtered the innocent baby at the gates of Hira. For anger is like a wound's blood which, unless it is staunched, will stain and spread till the whole cloak be crimson.'

The Twenty-fourth Story

LUQAIT THE EAGLE,
A STORY OF DREAMS

Luqait ibn Zahar of the Darem was a proud young warrior and a coxcomb who had usurped his father's influence in the tribe, and his arrogant behaviour was an affront to Arab magnanimity. Tall he was, and strong, and with a band of twelve riders he raided in the eastern desert around Darem. His insolence had earned him the name of 'The Eagle', and in truth he saw himself as superior to all other fighting men, just as an eagle soars high above all birds. His reputation brought harm to his people; and his father, in the evening of his days, spoke up, saying, 'O Luqait, you have indeed many gifts, but a true nobleman is known by his humility, and I must speak for all the tribe. Overbearing are you, and selfish to a fault. Why, my son, see how you strut and play before our people like a mating bustard, or a fine peacock from the palace of Chosroes. Truly, if a man owned a hundred flying camels, and if he had Badra al Yamaniya bint Muazzem for his bride, and if he had fought with 'Antar himself, then might he have cause to brag as you do, and flaunt his fine clothing and his fine-wrought armour. But you have done none of these things.'

And Luqait, angry and ashamed, would not answer his father, for he sensed the truth of these remarks; but overnight he left his people, taking with him only a small party and horses, and their tracks led towards the land of Az, where ruled the lord Muazzem of Nihas, Lord of the Pavilions.

Now the people of Az worshipped an idol upon the

mountainside, and the name of the idol was Jebbar; and at this time the idol was said to have demanded a sacrifice which was to be none other than Badra al Yamaniya, daughter of the lord Muazzem. All were grieved and much disturbed, though it is not known to this day whether this idol demanded the young girl as a slain sacrifice or to serve as a priestess in its sacred grove.

Az is a fair country of hills, grass-covered and with rocks and with water dripping from the fronds of green plants and the leaves of green trees, and here a man could for a time forget the rigours of the desert where naught may move or sound save the dry camel-thorn tossed by the errant wind. There are cities here, and Luqait came to the city and asked audience, but before seeing the lord Muazzem, Luqait laid aside his riding clothes and put on robes of great magnificence, scarlet-dyed, white and saffron, and he strode into the lord's meeting place up a staircase of shallow stone steps, as grand and as proud as an eagle riding the winds which fall and rise around the peaks and crevasses of the Yemeni mountains.

Now the lord Muazzem was disturbed by dreams which had distressed him over many nights, and it had become clear to him in these dreams that he would have to give up his beloved daughter to the idol Jebbar, and the high priest had only this day come to express the idol's desire for the services of this maiden. Yet also had he learnt to expect the arrival of a valiant hero, a fit husband for Bedra; even the name 'Luqait' was whispered within the dream. So, as Luqait mounted the long stairway, Muazzem thought to himself, If Bedra were not a maiden she would not be demanded of the dread Jebbar — if I were to marry her to this proud and beautiful young man, I might at least be sure to see her again, albeit in some distant land. For you must know, O listeners, that hitherto no man had satisfied Muazzem as a suitable consort for his daughter, neither had any man pleased Bedra.

So Muazzem received Luqait kindly, for all his guest's arrogant behaviour, and it was not long before the matter of marriage to Bedra was mooted by Luqait, and Muazzem was delighted, since it seemed to him that the gods themselves were working on his side; and the affair was settled to the advantage of all concerned. For although Bedra was not consulted formally, she could not but admire the lovely though tiresome young man who had come so far to seek her. Feasts were prepared, and when all the tribal customs were fulfilled, Luqait led Bedra to his own small tent, and because of the idol no mention was made by his hosts of the lack of a price, or dowry, for his bride.

Nevertheless, Luqait felt the shame of his poverty and he determined not to consummate the marriage until gifts had been exchanged; though, to be sure, such was his arrogance that it did not occur to him to inform his wife. And she pined and brooded, saying to herself, 'He loves me not.'

Luqait then, and his band of followers and his wistful bride, left these well-favoured lands, and Muazzem was sad to see them go, yet he rejoiced, for the dreams with which he had been tormented ceased, and he felt within himself that the will of the gods had been accomplished and that perhaps Jebbar was not so powerful an idol after all. And indeed it appeared that no particular misfortune descended upon the tribe and its cities and its fertile lands; and it is said that from that day the worship of the god Jebbar grew half-hearted. And Luqait, as he neared his native desert, felt his spirits rise, and he spoke to Bedra kindly, bidding her smile. And Bedra smiled. And at that moment Luqait, who had only entered into the marriage to spite his father, felt the arrows of true love pierce his heart. The Eagle was wounded now, and he whispered, 'O Bedra, you are beautiful indeed; and see, the desert wind has brought back colour to your pale face, and the desert sun has dried those mournful tears, and I cannot but love you.' For, indeed, this is what he believed had happened, since he could not, in his arrogance, envisage the true happiness of human companionship, the small beginnings of which had for Bedra brought joy in place of misery. Thereafter they rode together, and they spoke together all the long day, and by sundown Bedra had learned from her Eagle why he had not felt it right to consummate the marriage, and she was comforted.

Then of a sudden arose a threat which might have ended their new-found joy, for a wild figure leapt from among the rocks about the path, and his dark shadow raced towards them over the sand; and he challenged their progress with a spear. The wild man cursed and shouted. He shattered the golden calm of the desert evening, and a great fear descended upon the travellers as Luqait spurred against the stranger, for it was none other than Harith ibn Dhalim, and he seemed to carry with him an aroma of evil and perversion.

The two men fought there in the evening light, and Harith's mad strength ebbed from him as suddenly as it had surged, so that he surrendered his spear to Luqait; yet this was but a trick, and having edged his foe towards the rocks, Harith seized a hidden sword and wounded the Eagle warrior, even though the oath of surrender had been uttered and he was unarmed. Luqait's men could see that the combat was as unfair as the one between 'Antar and Ghasik ibn Ashab, he who tried in treachery to fight with darts, both combatants having agreed to remove blade from haft. It will be remembered that 'Antar had but a shaft to fight with, whereas Ghasik concealed three darts in his robes. Yet still did 'Antar triumph, felling Ghasik with the bare shaft. And so was it in this instance, for Luqait's men closed in upon the Impostor now, and disarmed him.

Now Luqait had decided to take his bride to Hira to the court of King Numan, there to let her lodge in safety while he strove to win the flying camels for a worthy brideprice; and now the two continued upon this way, and Harith with them, bound upon a horse. And when the journey was accomplished they crossed from the desert to the sown land, and there at the desert's edge was a burial ground — a place of desolation, and piled stones, and fluttering rags which might affright the jinns themselves. And Numan himself had come with offerings to be left upon two tombs. One was the tomb of Khaled ibn Jaafar of the Aamir, and the other the little grave of his son Shirjibeel. And the king wept.

Then, as he saw the small group of strangers approaching, he recognized Harith, and his face darkened in fear and anger to see again the man who had brought such horror to the kingdom of Hira; and Numan's mind was divided between sorrow and joy as he watched the slow approach of his enemy, bound and helpless upon a horse.

Later Numan held court, and stories were exchanged between him and Luqait, the Eagle Warrior; and Numan was touched by the beauty of Bedra al Yamaniya, and indeed he admired the valour of the handsome Eagle, though arrogance lay like a chasm between them still. Nevertheless, Numan acknowledged his debt to Luqait and gave him a thousand flying camels and many other rich gifts in exchange for the captive Harith.

The celebrations lasted seven days, and the assembled

'Muazzem was indeed glad to see the rich palanquin in which his daughter rode'

company feasted by the light of cooking-fires where great fish were stretched on iron spits against the blaze. And through the capture of Harith, Luqait had earned both wealth and prowess for himself, and he had won his bride and he had won his camels, and now he had only to find and challenge 'Antar to complete the tasks his father had set him.

But first he escorted his bride safely back to Muazzem's palace, and Muazzem was indeed glad to see the rich palanquin in which his daughter rode, and the horses and camels and slaves Luqait had won for her. And Muazzem was even more happy to see in his daughter's radiant face, and to hear in her youthful laughter, the essence of happiness so pure that many mortals never taste it in a life's span. But still Muazzem found his son-in-law both irritating and insolent, and he was glad to see him ride off to seek 'Antar.

Now just as Muazzem had been troubled with dreams about the dangers encompassing his daughter, so had Merweh bint Sheddad been worried by dreams about her son, Hatal. Merweh was a half-sister to 'Antar, whom she loved; but she quarrelled frequently with her husband Jahja. She loved, also, her son, who was very dear to his noble uncle 'Antar. At this time she sent messages to her half-brother, by way of Shiboob, saying, 'O my brother, there is bad blood between me and my husband, and between him and our son, and this I am accustomed to. Yet am I worried, for Hatal is no longer a boy but a young man, and he has taken to riding out at night with the Riders, and I fear for him. Moreover, my dreams have been of his capture, and now I believe he is indeed a prisoner for he has been absent many days. And yesterday a slave came begging bean husks, and he told me that a young man who might well have been Hatal had been seen bound in the company of Luqait ibn Zahar; he who is known as the Eagle Warrior because of his pride, and that they were heading towards Darem.' So 'Antar set off for Darem, and with him rode Sheddad and Shiboob and Jarir his brother, and the Karad horsemen, and Zakhmet al Jawad. And 'Antar planned to find the boy he loved, but he was anxious on account of Merweh's dreams.

So it was, O my listeners, that Luqait was searching for 'Antar and 'Antar was seeking for Luqait, who had indeed captured Hatal, so beloved of his mother, Merweh bint Sheddad.

Shiboob and Jarir would often accomplish, by skill and cunning, results which other men achieved only by confrontation and violence; and they now disguised themselves, and with their inborn knowledge of the desert ways and wells they came swiftly to Luqait's camp, and they played the part of messengers from Ahmed ibn Jaafar, brother of the murdered Khaled.

Shiboob said to Luqait, 'Greetings, Eagle among the warriors. I am come to warn you that the warrior 'Antar is seeking you, since he believes that you have taken his beloved nephew Hatal into captivity. Hand him over to me, sir, as a safeguard. For there is enmity between my people and the Abs on account of Zuhair's death and the death of Shas. Yet was the murder of Khaled the act of one who seemed a friend of no man and an enemy of all. And it may well be that 'Antar is not to blame for it. This I can discover from Hatal.' And so it was arranged, and Hatal was delivered to Shiboob, who learned also that Harith was a prisoner. And Shiboob gave false directions to Luqait, who set off with a large force to seek 'Antar and did not find him; whereas Jarir rode direct to his noble half-brother, and the Abs raiders then welcomed Hatal, and they threatened those whom Luqait had left behind, but did them little harm since they would not plunder so small a company. 'Antar took only a few animals from among the flocks, and a few slaves, thus conveying to Luqait his displeasure at the capture of Hatal.

But now the conflict spread over the land in many an unexpected way, as the waters of a sudden flood may spread when the wadi widens, circling here and there, lapping one stone and leaving another dry, till finally the torrent drains into the sand and is gone. For Ahmed, spurred on by Gheshm the Spear-thrower, attacked and conquered many of the Abs, though Qais the warrior fled to Ghitafan and Fazara; and 'Antar and Shiboob, returning with their small forces, found themselves confronted by an army of six thousand Aamir men and others — and among these was none other than Luqait. Then there followed a battle which men remember to this day, so terrible was the carnage, and 'Antar fought like a lion. Yet were they pressed, he and Hatal and Shiboob, Jarir and Sheddad and the Karad horsemen, and Zakhmet al Jawad.

Meanwhile, in Hira, a shadow had fallen between Mutajerida and Numan the king, and the perfidy of Harith ibn Dhalim seemed to spread like sickness, infecting one after

173

another among his associates. Mutajerida knew of Harith's capture by Luqait, and she knew where Numan had him confined; and she thought little of the murder of Khaled, for had he not killed her brother and her father, or at least been responsible for their killings? But worse, she hid from her mind the horrid killing of Numan's infant son, erasing the thought from her consciousness when it would try to enter, and thus in some measure sharing in the sickness of Harith. She sent her own slaves to free Harith by night. And with the slaves she sent a message bidding him fly to the Abs camp and bargain with Qais for freedom and, perchance, a return to al Murra. And she furnished him with horses.

So it happened that, while the fighting spread over the land like the Great River itself in flood and destruction, and while 'Antar battled against Ahmed and Luqait together, the day was saved for the Abs people by the appearance of an army of men, fresh and vigorous, and with Qais at their head. Then, as the Aamir turned to the new force, a third invaded their ranks, for Harith, boasting of his dark and unmanly deeds, rode like a whirlwind to rescue the Abs people, and with their help, and with arms taken from the slain, the day was won. Ahmed fled, and Luqait led his men from the field in good array, and fast, but doubtful now of the advisability of complying with the third of his father's conditions, for he could see that 'Antar was no mean warrior. And Luqait repented of his rashness in provoking a battle for no better reason than fame and renown.

'Indeed, here is a man whom all must acknowledge,' Luqait said to his followers, 'and we have no place in quarrels between the Abs and the Aamir.' And he returned home much the wiser to his lovely bride, and to the wealth he had won through the capture of Harith for Numan.

And as for Harith, the Abs leaders could not deny him protection, for had he not saved their men in trouble, and who could say as yet whether the dark tales told of his exploits in Hira and beyond Hira were indeed true? Yet none could trust Harith, or love him; and in his own troubled mind Harith despised and hated them all. Fear of Numan alone brought him to humiliate himself in association with Qais and with 'Antar; and he knew in his heart that all the peoples of Arabia united together could not save him from himself.

The Twenty-fifth Story
'ANTAR'S DOUBTS AND FEARS

It may well seem strange, O my listeners, to tell a story of 'Antar's doubts and fears, yet must this be done, for although in his marriage to 'Abla he had reached the heights of bliss which some would have thought reserved for paradise, and although 'Abla's happiness was complete, yet there remained certain misgivings, certain apprehensions which beset them both.

It came about then that 'Antar found himself a prey to melancholy. Wherever he looked about him he could see naught but savagery and war. For his own tribe, he feared nothing more than fruitless conflict with King Numan; and for his own self, he doubted the integrity of his old enemies, Malec and Amr, Rabia and Amara. Though Malec would sometimes smile upon the lovers, none could be sure of his true feelings.

'Antar — fearing — knew that Rabia had told King Numan how the Abs had given shelter to Harith ibn Dhalim. 'Antar — doubting — came, an unwilling guest, to an open-air feast on the shores of Dhat al Arsad's pools at Malec's invitation.

It was night, and the stars blazed in the sky but were dimmed by the glinting light of cooking-fires, and both stars and sparks were reflected in the rippling waters. Food there was, and wine to spare, and maidens dancing, but 'Antar and Shiboob were ill at ease, and with reason. For as the feast ended, when all might be off their guard, horsemen were heard, and Rabia and Hadifa and many others swept down upon the revellers in a treacherous attempt to capture 'Antar.

175

In the fighting 'Antar and Shiboob saved themselves, but the rest fled, and Malec, wounded and defeated in this ignoble attempt to trap his own son-in-law, rode off in the darkness with Amr and the other men. So the old divisions in the tribe were reawakened, and 'Antar, for all his anger, wept at the lakeside, crying:

'How great is the perfidy of man.
How long-lasting is his hatred, and his jealousy.
How strong envy is: how powerful the longing for revenge.
Who can conquer perfidy and hatred, jealousy and envy;
    who can drain away
The poisonous blister from the mind longing for revenge,
Drain away the poison, as a man sucks poison
        From a viper's stabbing,
        From the double stabbing of a scorpion's sting?'

When the dawn broke the brothers returned to their camps and their tents, and they found that Hadifa had been there before them, and had already complained bitterly to Qais. 'Truly, my lord and friend,' he had said, 'I came but to visit you, yet was I set upon by 'Antar who was feasting and revelling by the well's edge, being drunk with wine. Moreover,' added Hadifa, 'he has injured Rabia also,' And he told a false story of 'Antar's exploits in the Yemen. But 'Antar told the true story of Rabia's night ambush, and Qais believed him, and Qais knew moreover that the Yemeni tales were but bitter attempts of Rabia's to blacken 'Antar's name. So the bond between 'Antar and his lord was strengthened.

Now 'Abla was sorely distressed by the behaviour of her father and her brother, and she wept, saying to 'Antar, 'O my husband, you deserved better than this in marrying me. Yet would I beg you to find my father, foolish and wicked though he has been, for my sake.' And 'Antar's heart softened and he left to search for those who had plotted to harm him.

Now it happened that after the conflict Hadifa and Rabia had taken one path, and Malec and Amr another; and Malec and Amr had fallen into the hands of the Jibhan people, and they were imprisoned in the valley of Zerud. Messengers had been sent to Ahmed in Hira, and to Luqait in the Yemen, inviting them to come and witness the deaths of these two Abs leaders. So 'Antar, apprised of this by the desert birds, rode with his companions, Sheddad and Urwah and Harith and others, to the valley. And there all remained hidden while only 'Antar and Shiboob crept within earshot of the prisoners and their captors.

And now a strange thing happened, for the captives were bound and helpless by the fireside, and Ramih ibn Saba of the Jibhan and his men surrounded them, and the whole assembly was listening to poetry declaimed by a party of itinerant shepherds who had been given good food and water in return for the entertainment they could provide. As 'Antar and Shiboob listened, they heard one of the shepherds say, 'O my lords and benefactors, here, then, is the famous story of the archer and the fawn.' And he proceeded to declaim this noble poem. And when he came to the lines:

> Then did the swift archer raise his silver knife.
>
> Yet, as he raised it, from the fawn's dark eyes,
> Tears fell, upon the hand which gripped its throat,
> And as a man bemused, the archer saw not the smooth,
>   delicate fawn,
>   But saw his own love, who, when he left her last,
>   Had wept for their mutual loss,
> And, weeping, had let fall silver tears
> Upon the hands which gently cupped her face ... '

— then did the company weep in sympathy, deeply moved by the story of the archer who released the fawn because it was as beautiful as his loved one. And above all the voices rose that of Malec, who cried, 'Alas for my mean and ungrateful behaviour, that poem was the work of my noble son-in-law and is like to be my death-knell. If he were but here to listen to my repentance he would hear my vows of true friendship, but it is too late.' For Malec hoped that the shepherd was perhaps a messenger of 'Antar's in disguise, though his hopes were unfounded.

And 'Antar and Shiboob exchanged silent glances of astonishment at the recitation of 'Antar's own poem.

Now small trees grew in profusion in the Zerud valley, and as the night darkened 'Antar and Shiboob each collected a vast bundle of wood branches; and in the dawn they approached the prisoners disguised as village men who depend upon firewood, and they hurled their loads upon the fire. The

177

flames leapt up in the centre of the encampment, causing much confusion as dogs barked and women called and men tried to prevent the sparks and the glowing embers from firing their precious tents; and during this confusion 'Antar and Shiboob cut the bonds of Malec and Amr, and they fled to the perimeter of the camp where horses were awaiting them. Then 'Antar fought against the whole tribe, allowing the others time to mount and fly. And he killed Ramih, and escaped safely with the rest. And he and Malec were reconciled, and Malec wept; for in truth he was an old man and in his old age he recognized his son-in-law's true worth, and he found humility and real comfort at last in his daughter's choice.

So that never again could 'Antar say, as he had said in the past, 'Alas, any good I may do him seems but to increase his scorn and hatred.'

So the men from Hira and the men from the Yemen, coming to see vengeance wrought upon Malec by the Jibhan, encountered only the remnants of the tribe in flight, and they turned and rode home disappointed. But 'Antar rejoiced in his final acceptance by the repentant Malec. And he rode home to his beloved 'Abla.

Then there occurred a happening, O my listeners, which led to further troubles among the tribes. Those of you who remember the story of the perfect colt, Dahis the Thruster, who was ordained by the gods to come to birth despite the efforts of his dam's master to abort the implanted seed of his existence, will also perhaps remember that a certain confusion arose about the story; for some said they heard it from 'Abla's lips when she was but a child, and others that Shiboob himself took part in the great race between Dahis and Hadifa's mare, Ghabra.

Now there was — or there was not — such a race; and this was the way of it. Qais had wished to buy the colt Dahis from his friend, leader of the Riyan, who owned it; yet was Kerim incensed, for, as an Arab of honour, he would have given Qais the colt had the desire but been expressed. Trouble arose then between the Abs and the Riyan, and Qais obtained Dahis by force and looked upon his lovely colt as a man looks upon his first love, grooming him daily with his own hands. And Rabia and Hadifa envied Qais and plotted even his death in their agony of spite. And much ill-will and evil-doing accompanied the great race between Dahis and Ghabra, and bets were won and lost, and it is even recounted — though I for one, O my listeners, will never believe it — that 'Antar, returning to the camp, hurried to see Dahis before even approaching 'Abla's tents.

Passions then ran high between the Abs and Fazara and the Riyan; and moreover, 'Antar's fears of war between his people and Numan's were at this time increased. For Sinan came from Hira, demanding the return of Harith ibn Dhalim. (How this man's shadow darkened all it touched!) Yet could Qais not agree to Harith's abandonment. And the two Fazara brothers, Hadifa and Haml, quarrelled openly over the issue. Hadifa condemned Qais, but Haml admired his adherence to the accepted rule of Arab tradition.

Yet was Qais far from happy over the affair since Harith's murder of the infant Shirjibeel had now been heard by all, and it would never be forgotten or condoned. And Sinan, too, added to the confusion by pretending to seek asylum with the Abs, whereas in reality he came to divide the tribes into factions for Numan's benefit.

So when the day of the race came, all was set for trouble and confusion, and 'Antar addressed the crowd, crying to them: 'Let us support Qais in this contest between the two noble steeds, Dahis, who runs for my lord, and Hadifa's mare Ghabra. And listen, O Hadifa of the Fazara peoples, as I warn you not in any way to impede the horse against the mare.'

Shiboob, too, seeking to calm the emotions which ran so high, announced amid laughter that he would beat both horses running on foot, losing fifty camels should he be beaten, and taking a hundred camels should he win. And, indeed, in the race Shiboob kept ahead of both the famed contestants — so the story goes — and still he found time to attack and kill Hadifa's servant, Damis, who sought to hinder the colt by a stone flung against his forehead. Thus — it is said — to everyone's amazement Shiboob passed first between the two lances, then Ghabra came, unharmed, and only then Dahis with bruised forehead and streaming eyes. As for Damis the servant, he never came at all, for he was dead. And although Shiboob slaughtered twenty of the camels he won by his amazing victory and gave a great feast to the poor and the widows and the orphans among the many spectators, many dared not approach the feast, for they thought, 'Here surely is a sorcerer.' And Qais was furious over Dahis's injuries, whereas

Hadifa was angry over Ghabra's defeat, and over the murder of his servant Damis.

All might have calmed down had an element of mystification and merriment remained in the hearts of the spectators and the leaders of the tribes, but the gods decreed otherwise, and a spark which could have been extinguished by good will and good chance blazed now into a fire not to be quenched. For Hadifa's son, Abi Firaqa, came with demands from Hadifa to Qais, and with messages full of anger and reproach, over the wagers, the race itself and the participants. And Abi Firaqa approached Qais as his anger was abating, and Qais said: 'Nay, my son, your father is enraged, as I have been; yet is there little between us. Stay then overnight and present your messages in the cool of the morning. Maybe we can come to some agreement.' And Abi Firaqa stayed. Yet in the morning it was as though he had changed his mind and become all perversity, for he harangued Qais with disrespect and discourtesy, and threatened force if his demands were not met. And indeed, O my listeners, history teaches us that this is a very dangerous attitude for any messenger to take up, and Abi Firaqa paid the penalty. For Qais's fury boiled within him and he struck the boy dead with his spear. Then he caused the body to be bound upon a horse, and he sent the horse with its tragic burden at a gallop to the Fazara camp. And all hope of further peace seemed lost, for this was a dreadful deed.

Seldom had such darkness fallen upon the two neighbouring tribes, the Abs and the Fazara. And now foolish men encouraged bitterness and hatred on each side, playing upon the grief and agony of Hadifa and upon the rage and pride of Qais. Yet the very horror of the act brought sense to those who had so recently allowed passions to mount too high over a mere race. Harith returned to his Murra people to avoid involvement. And Rabia headed north and west on a long-planned visit to the Beni Ghassan, those who for so long had followed the teachings of the Prophet Issa and worshipped him as a god. And Rabia knew he could not fight his own people, though he had no compunction in waging war against 'Antar for what he considered the good of the tribe. Qais, in cold appraisal of his own rash act, and in remorse, summoned his men about him; and Hadifa, weary and implacably angry, called council of his own.

And a solution was sought through combat between the two

men, Qais on Dahis and Hadifa on Ghabra; and the two tribes gathered in silence to watch the contest.

Yet was destruction not to fall upon them, for the elders of both tribes spoke and prayed together, and they read the omens and they could see how a war of this nature might deprive them all of liberty and of life itself. And the religious men approached the leaders, and the leaders themselves conferred and sought a reasonable issue of the conflict while yet the two men fought upon horseback. So when darkness was falling propositions were presented to the two men, the lord Qais and the lord Hadifa, weary and battle-scarred as they were, by the elders who came to intervene. And they came bare headed and bare foot, and they bore the idols of the tribes upon their shoulders (for this was in the time of Ignorance before the Prophet — upon whom be peace — had taught us submission to the One God). And men say there never was such a scene as that of the reconciliation between the Abs and the Fazara. Hadifa's grief was greater than his anger, and he accepted the blood-money proffered for his son's murder. And Qais's remorse at his impatience with youth was greater than his pride, and he offered recompense with the magnanimity worthy of an Arab prince, and the two men embraced. And Haml said to his brother in private, 'Indeed, my dear brother, this tragic happening is the result in no small measure of your own dishonesty in the great race.'

So was peace restored amid much rejoicing and feasting, and Qais sent Hadifa over and above the amount of the blood-money ordained by the elders, no less than two hundred camels and ten horses and twenty slaves. Thus it was that another of 'Antar's fears was put to rest, and the shadow of Harith ibn Dhalim lifted, for a time, from the community.

The Twenty-sixth Story
THE PRINCE IN LOVE

How strange a thing it was, the ascendance of Malik the Prince among the sons of Zuhair and among the tribe. In sorrow and in joy, in ill-doing and in well-doing, all except the foolish ones turned to him for guidance. To 'Antar he was a magnet, a source of all noble impulse, the one who loved and who could rightly receive love, the wise man to whom life's meaning was apparent, its music plucking at a chord within his own being, its pattern fixed in the mind's eye like that traced by the wheeling stars whose high music throbs in the luminous night and yet is only heard by a few.

The Prince, the watcher, the observing one — for all his hatred of conflict and his love of mankind — had never, so it was believed, known in himself the radiance of love between man and woman. Indeed, he had often confided in 'Antar that to him the heights and depths of passion seemed unattainable, and he had come to think of love as folly. 'Although,' he would add, 'perhaps in the very folly of other men, and of women, do I find my rewards. For herein is their greatest need, and here my greatest chance to help them.' For the Prince was all benevolence.

Now it happened one day that 'Antar and the Prince and his brother, Harith ibn Zuhair, rode out from their camp upon a hunting trip. The camels' grazing was sparse that year, and summer had come too early, so the tribe had found its way into unfamiliar country, and the hunters were soon lost, and they panted in the heat of the sun, which beat as with rods upon the high desert. And their horses stumbled over the burning stones. Then they came to a wadi where, in season, a river would run through the white sand. But the time was past, though some shade could be found here against the sun's enmity.

After resting they went on their way, and they disturbed a small encampment and were welcomed there with the true hospitality of the desert dweller to whom the stranger and the traveller are as his own people. And here they drank sweet water, dipped from a hidden well among the pink flowers of the oleanders. And they rested there in the Valley of the Tamarisks, guests of the Ghorab people, who had so long ago helped Zuhair to capture Temadhur.

Then, as the shadows lengthened over the valley sand and crept up the rocky cliffs which hemmed them in, and as the opalescent colours of evening glowed and changed over each smallest object, a girl came down the wadi to the well, and she filled her pitcher at the clear fountain and returned as she had come, graceful and upright, bearing the pitcher now upon her head.

The Prince had watched such an occurrence nearly every evening of his life, yet had he displayed no special interest other than to muse, from time to time, upon the nature of water, or the division of labour within the tribe; but on this evening, in the short dusk, his whole life was changed by overwhelming love for the maiden of the pitcher.

It became clear overnight, to 'Antar and his aggrieved companions, that no further hunting would be possible, for the Prince spent the dark hours in consultation with the leader of the Ghorab whose daughter had so bewitched him; and the maiden herself was summoned, and although startled by the suddenness of his approach, she looked favourably on the man to whom all seemed to owe a special reverence. So after a short delay for a few simple rejoicings, the two parted so that presents might be sought and exchanged and ceremonies completed.

And as 'Antar and the Prince rode home to their summer camp, 'Antar said, 'O my friend, here is a change indeed from the days when you would reproach 'Abla and myself for the folly of our love!' And 'Antar joked; but the Prince was silent, happy-hearted, and hearing nothing save the voice of his beloved whispering good-bye. She seemed to him as lovely and perhaps as transient a thing as a rainbow which lightens the heart after the winter rains but which can never be caught even by the swiftest rider. Yet had he held her hand in his and felt the glow of her presence in his heart.

When the hunters returned there was much astonishment and merriment at the plight of the Prince, and Qais chaffed him about his choice, saying, 'O my brother, I am happy in your happiness, but have we not maidens among the Abs with whom you could be united? The Ghorab are but a small people and subservient to us. Indeed, I remember that our father constrained them to bring about his own marriage with our mother, and the actions to which they agreed were of doubtful morality!' But the Prince smiled, saying after a pause so long that Qais thought he had never heard the question, 'O Qais, my brother, what are you saying? Love is of the one God and is not of our choosing.' And 'Antar added, 'Indeed, my lord Qais, the Prince is right, and in the Ghadha valley he has found true love. Here was no violence and no oppression and no guile — only sweetness and understanding.'

Presents were then prepared for the maiden of the pitcher and her parents, and the Prince followed upon his heralds, and the marriage took place all the more joyfully for being so unexpected. And when the feasting and the music were at their height and the lovely Jamila came as a bride to the Prince's tent, his happiness was so intense that all who saw him as he welcomed her were struck by the shining joyousness of his countenance; and one guest said to another, 'He has the look of an immortal.' And this was how he would be remembered.

For, following upon the ardour which had seemed to sweep the Prince to the very summit of happiness, there came, swift as a hawk's stoop, misery which cast his bride and his companions into the shadows or despair, just as a traveller who, so nearly achieving the sunlit reaches of a mountain pass, may yet miss his foothold and fall with a cry into some dark crevasse, his hands gripping empty air, and may find death before the echoes of his voice are stilled.

For before dawn broke upon the Ghorab camp, a band of men came stealthily to the perimeter, advancing in silence, and the watchmen saw them not for they had drunk and feasted with the rest. And when 'Antar woke and summoned all to their defence it was too late — the leader had made his way into the nuptial tent and roughly disturbed the Prince,

184

who lay there with his bride, their bed scented with aromatic herbs as is the custom.

Now the Prince pursued the raiders from the tent, and both attackers and defenders ceased from the fight to see the outcome — yet could there be but one issue from this infamous attack, for the raider was armed and alert, and the Prince bemused with passion and slumber. And as the sun's rays touched his raised hand and his dagger with gold, he was struck down at the tent's door. Then the raiders fled, but none followed; for 'Antar leapt to the aid of his prince and bene-factor, his friend. But nothing that he or the women of the tribe could do would staunch the blood flowing from terrible wounds, and before the sun was high in the sky the Prince died in his bride's arms, his face wet with her tears.

Now the dark raider had been no other than Hadifa, himself half-maddened by the death of his own son. And this was the story of his revenge. Though he had made his peace with Qais yet was his grief unbearable, and his wife Badra would not agree to the peace which had been made between the two tribes. And she despised Haml and Qais for the truce, seeing nothing noble in their motives but thinking only that her son's life was worth more than a few camels (in which she was right) — and, in her grief, not caring that further conflict could bring misery to the mothers of other sons.

So she wept and railed at all who tried to comfort her, and she refused even to speak to Hadifa, and she abused Haml unmercifully for what she saw as his coward's part in the tragedy of death. Verses, too, she made for her grief's sake, though not for her comfort, for comfort seemed to her a weakness. And she did not see that her sorrow was indeed becoming the seed of a great and spreading tree of hatred — high-spreading, deep-rooted and casting an unwelcome shade. Poets in after years would shudder at her malignant words, yet would weep at those of Jamila who, widowed in the very dawn after her wedding night, whispered:

> 'The head I bore upon my breast
> Lies now, heavy, upon my arm.
> Blood soaks my sleeve;
>   And tears for my lost love —
> Whom I could love only so briefly, so briefly
> — Tears dim my eyes, as his are closed in death.'

'The Prince died in his bride's arms'

Now Hadifa, too, shuddered at his wife's malevolence, yet did he try to soothe her, but the evil spread between them; and so a plot was hatched to wreak vengeance upon the Abs by murdering their guide and benefactor at the very height of his happiness. And this was the tragic motive which brought Hadifa and his men to such action. When it had been accomplished they fled unmolested, but greatly fearing the wrath of 'Antar and Qais. And Haml the Peacemaker, who had known nothing of the affair, greeted his brother only with silence and reproach.

Grief overwhelmed all the Abs people when the wedding party returned in mourning, and the whole tribe seemed crushed under the sorrow they had to bear. Qais and Temadhur spoke of vengeance for the murder, but 'Antar's sorrow was such that he made no move and contributed in no way to a decision. He spent his days and his nights at the Prince's tomb.

Yet some believe the gods leave us comfort still in our disasters, and from this grim fatality they brought reconciliation between Rabia and Qais; and even between Rabia and 'Antar. For Hadifa, returning harassed, told not only Haml but Rabia of his vengeance, for Rabia had returned from his long journey among the Syrian, the Christian, tribes. And Haml's anxious silence contrasted with Rabia's furious contempt and heartfelt grief. So strong had been the ascendance of the Prince that even Rabia had felt the pull of his nobility; and hearing of the murder his sorrow was loosed like a flood, and he stormed out from Hadifa's tent. Then calling upon his followers, who had so often sheltered with the Fazara people, Rabia leapt to his horse and rode at speed to the Abs camp.

There, seeing Qais and the leaders in consultation, he came among them weeping and with torn garments, and he walked barefoot to the tomb where 'Antar was, and the two were at last reconciled.

Qais indeed still distrusted his nephew, yet was he convinced later of Rabia's genuine sorrow, for his very slaves bore witness to it, saying: 'Our lord finds now no comfort save in poetry.' And Rabia's poem on sleep and sorrow is remembered to this day; and so intense was the feeling expressed therein that Qais knew there could be no doubt of Rabia's change of heart towards them all, perhaps the last benison laid upon them through the goodness of the Prince.

And so the month which had begun in such delight and wonderment ended in sadness, and there were those among the Abs who thought 'Antar would lose his reason through this, the worst loss he had sustained. Yet did 'Abla guide her consort through the shadows which engulfed them all; and Rabia, watching him with new eyes, felt that some guidance came to 'Antar still. It was as though the ghost of the dead Prince lingered for a little time by the desolate tomb, held in fetters of love given and love received.

The Twenty-seventh Story

THE CRIMES OF HARITH AND HADIFA

So bitter had become the quarrel between the Abs and the Fazara that Harith ibn Dhalim withdrew to his own people, uncertain of his way forward. For to him conflict was but a means to his own advancement, and he saw in the struggles of his life no clash of honour and dishonour, no choice of good or evil, no battle of loyalties.

And Hadifa lived, and indeed was to die, within the traditions of his people, yet was he pricked on by hatred, and closed his mind and heart to magnanimity and merriment. And so, O my listeners, these two men, Hadifa and Harith, brought destruction and disaster to the tribes.

'Antar — prompted, some say, by the spirit of the Prince lingering with his loved ones — restored to the sad widow that dower which Beni Fazara men had filched from her when they killed her husband. And this enraged Hadifa anew, and his men marched against the Abs, and a battle was fought upon the sandhills of Muraiqib.

Now Qais and 'Antar and all the men of Abs fought nobly on this day, for they feared the advance of King Numan's armies, whom they must also needs meet, from the north; and on the second day of the battle they gained ascendancy, and Sinan spoke to Hadifa, saying, 'O Hadifa, you are too precipitate, and should have awaited the forces of my lord Numan, who also has a quarrel to settle with these dogs. See, I will by a trick enable you to retire in honour and await their coming.'

So on the morning of the second day Sinan ran between the

opposing forces, bareheaded and with his garments rent; and the elders on each side supported him, and a truce ensued. Then was an arrangement made, that the Fazara should not participate in fighting between the Abs and Numan, and as a surety more than two hundred Fazara children came as hostage to the Abs camp, and were welcomed there with kindness. But Hadifa did not hold this promise sacred in his heart, and all this while there was no word of Harith ibn Dhalim.

Then news came that Numan's armies were near by, led by Prince Aswad and with many famed leaders among them: Luqait and Gheshm and others. So it was that Qais and 'Antar advanced to meet them, leaving but a few men to guard their camp since the threat from the Fazara had been averted and promises made and witnessed by the elders.

Yet had they not conceived of the infamy of Hadifa, whose savage anger was now increased by the death, at her own hands, of his wife Badra. Driven by some madness, just as she had been, he sent a party to the Abs camp to bring back the hostage Fazara children; and this they did. But before returning they slaughtered four hundred of the Abs children, leaving them dead upon the ground; and those who survived fled into the desert, and the men left to guard them lost each one his life against bitter odds.

Now the anguish of this day's wickedness was something to stop the heart beating, and who can describe the sorrow which was, and which was to come? The innocent ones suffered here, as we are told by the wise Jews the innocent suffered under their king Herod when the Prophet Issa was but newly born. And these peoples of the Book tell us that vengeance is of the one God, but though many deeds may be remembered with pride in the long and tangled history of the tribes, Hadifa's massacre brought upon his men a vengeance which the Abs people could themselves with gratitude forget. But they cannot. For later they captured those who had done this thing, and gave them over to the women of the Abs to kill, in their own way, with little hands.

Now the Abs forces, in ignorance yet of this grim disaster, advanced north till they were within a half-day's march of Numan's armies; and here they met Harith ibn Dhalim with a small party of raiders, and Harith said, 'O Qais, it is through my fault that Numan marches against you in such strength, and see, I am come to help you in the fight.' But Qais, though he welcomed a clever fighter, could neither trust nor love this dark man.

Then the two armies circled and skirmished, testing each the strength of the other, and Gheshm was taken prisoner by 'Antar. And Shiboob sought to avoid a great battle, and he disguised himself as a messenger from the Fazara and slipped through the lines, seeking an audience with Prince Aswad. Then he said, 'O prince, Hadifa my lord is on the march to help you, and begs you to await his coming, for like your noble self he wishes to ensure the capture and death not only of 'Antar the black slave, but also of Harith ibn Dhalim, who, though he has sheltered with our people, now fights with the Abs and has done much evil, we hear, in your far kingdom.' And Prince Aswad was deceived and his forces dispersed in the desert, and they were separated, the one group from the other, so that on Shiboob's return Qais was enabled to attack with skill. And both Luqait and Prince Aswad were captured.

Yet then came messengers from the Abs: two youths who had escaped the massacre had been sent by the distraught women to tell of this disaster. And 'Antar and Qais, grim in their grief and only half-believing, turned for home. And they left Harith to bring in the prisoners more slowly, for they themselves and all their men sped swiftly south. Yet, not trusting Harith, they told him nothing of the massacre, giving him other reasons for their hasty departure.

When they came to the camp those who had fled were returning, but Qais and 'Antar would leave no woman nor child in tent or shelter in that place, and they moved them to a hidden valley, for none could bear the familiar scene where once the children played. And later from this hidden place the men of Abs rode against the Fazara and singled out the murderers of their children, as has been told.

Now Harith travelled slowly with his prisoners, and he came to the old camp and found it desolate, bare to the winds and the ashes of its fires scattered, and he was astonished. He therefore waited three days and three nights, expecting news from Qais, but none came. Then Harith spoke with his prisoners Luqait and Gheshm and Prince Aswad, and a new concept came into his clever and impatient mind, and he thought, Truly, if I remain here in ignorance I work against myself. But should I escort these noble prisoners to Numan I could bargain for my own safety, and join with Fazara, too, against Abs, if needs be. And in his treachery he released Prince Aswad and the rest; and they journeyed together towards Hira.

Now it happened that, as they went, Prince Aswad seemed to gain ascendancy over his companions' minds, for though he was a hard man and a resolute fighter, yet was he honest, and once the demands of morality were satisfied he would bear no grudge and plot no evil. And he and his friends shrank from Harith, and Prince Aswad spoke for all of them when he said, 'O Harith, we are indeed indebted to you for our freedom and will not forget your due, neither will King Numan. Yet would we know why Abs have abandoned the struggle, and what delays Fazara; for we must regroup our scattered forces and attack again. Take then half your men and reconnoitre, and we will continue to Hira with the rest.' So it was, and the men of Hira felt that a shadow had lifted when Harith turned from among them.

Now 'Antar and Qais had divided their forces also, and 'Antar was in the northern desert, searching for Harith and the prisoners, all of whom had left traces of their occupation at the Camp of the Massacre, but who had vanished thereafter; and Qais was in the south harrying Hadifa. But the main Abs forces remained in the new camp, rebuilding their lives after the killing of the innocents, and these were dark days.

'Antar then came upon his prisoners and recaptured them before they crossed into the sown land, and he treated them with honour as is the way of the Arabs, and he learned from them of Harith's treachery. So he returned to help Qais, and sure enough he found the Abs and the Fazara once more engaged in battle, and Harith now fighting on Hadifa's side. And Harith had sent for his brother, Cosrua, and certain others of the Murra people, enlisting their help. But 'Antar spoke to the Murra, crying aloud, 'Nay, O men of the Murra, and you, O Cosrua, before joining in battle against us, hear what has occurred.' And he told them of Harith's crimes and of Hadifa's crimes, and truly it seemed to all his listeners, so vivid was his language (for he was above all a poet), as though Harith's banefulness and Hadifa's viciousness mingled, weaving like two dark threads a hideous pattern in the web of all their lives. Then did Cosrua, brother of Harith, cry, 'O Harith, you have violated the precepts which regulate our living and our dying, and you have brought disorder among us: and I cannot engage Murra in battle on the side of Hadifa or of yourself.' For truly Cosrua was an intrepid and an upright man. But Harith would not be thwarted; and to the horror of all gathered there — Murra, Abs and Fazara alike — he rushed suddenly upon his brother and killed him, with no warning and with no challenge. And they were true brothers, of one blood. And all shuddered at the impiety of this desperate action.

Then did Sheddad mount upon his horse, and he challenged Harith, crying, 'O traitor, what have you done! Turn then and defend yourself in honour!' And the two men fought, and Harith was a clever fighter and Sheddad was wounded; but evening was falling then, and the Murra men called to their leader, 'O Harith, you have killed our true leader Cosrua, whom we loved, your own blood brother. You can gain no honour in our eyes fighting an old man — turn against his son 'Antar if you would win our allegiance.'

And Harith heard them and ceased from the fighting, assisting Sheddad, in the gathering dusk, to his own tent, and feigning courtesy. But when 'Antar came to support his father, Harith treacherously struck out, slashing 'Antar's sword arm so that the blood mingled with that of his old father. Then, as Harith mounted and galloped off, 'Antar swore a great oath and challenged him to mortal combat when dawn should break. And all were sickened by the betrayal they had witnessed. The Abs and the Murra feared for the wounded 'Antar challenging such a clever fighter; and the Fazara watched in silence. But Harith cursed both friend and foe as he fled the camp, riding as if to the wind's end; for he began to see that he had lost support on all sides. And when he crept back in the darkness, he could find but ten men loyal to him, and he had no stomach for the morning's fight with 'Antar. So he and his little band of followers, with but a few camels, were gone long before the morning star paled in the sun's bright radiance.

And Aswad turned to 'Antar as warmth flooded back after the chill of a desert night, and he said, 'Truly, O my captor, we have scores to settle between us; but let us settle them as knights, and not as knaves or madmen such as are Hadifa and Harith ibn Dhalim.'

The Twenty-eighth Story
THE TRIBE IS SECURED

And now, O my listeners, we come to the end of our stories; for just as the marriage of 'Antar and 'Abla brought them both to true manhood and womanhood, so now do the plots and counterplots among the tribes bring them into that fellowship which 'Antar once thought beyond his reach; and to leadership in war and in poetry. And indeed, another plot is woven here, a plan more subtle and more marvellous than anything man could have devised, a revelation bringing with it the ending of the time of Ignorance.

But first we must hear how Harith ibn Dhalim fared when he fled, despondent and afraid, to Mecca. For while others in the Sacred Groves purified their minds and sought such peace and contentment as they could find, Harith was bent only upon conflict and unrest as he plotted how best to avenge himself upon his many enemies. And he paced up and down the trodden ways of Mecca, observed and avoided by all comers. Yet there was one who came close, and who recognized him. And this was Amr ibn Atnaba from the city of Yathrib. And a quarrel arose between them, for Amr knew Harith as the murderer of Khaled and of the child Shirjibeel. Later Harith left the groves, but he waited in ambush for Amr ibn Atnaba and murdered him by the wayside. And now even the ten men who had come with him to the groves deserted him, for they could not stomach these secret killings, and Harith found himself alone. And he said within himself, 'They do not understand.'

Now the cruelty and treachery of Harith during his last days with the Fazara and the Abs had greatly moved the two tribes; and both leaders had in revulsion sought to patch up a peace between themselves. Hadifa called down a curse upon his erstwhile friend, and 'Antar and Qais had long resolved to have nothing more to do with him should he reappear. And certain groups among the tribesmen fought and skirmished for eleven more days, but then some sort of truce was contrived by the leaders and the fighting ceased; and a great celebration and feast was planned to take place on the slopes of Sherebah.

But before this Hadifa asked of Qais, 'O Qais, we have had too long a period of strife and still are threatened, it may be, with more — until your quarrel with Numan is ended. Let then the Prince Aswad return to his brother to see if peace may be concluded in Hira also.' And this was done. So that when Harith, lonely and afraid, crept after a long journey into Prince Aswad's dwellings in that city, the Prince had returned a free man to his brother's court.

But on his travels Harith ibn Dhalim had committed a further crime, and one which was finally to bring him to judgement; and it came about thus:

Riding over wild country, rocky and dark, avoiding the sand desert which a man may not cross if he be alone, he came upon a brother and his sister living simply in their tents, tending a few sheep and goats and growing melons by a tiny spring. Harith rested there and welcomed their hospitality, for these were generous young people and virtuous, and they saw no evil in their companion since none dwelt in their own minds or hearts, and being youthful, experience had taught them little of the evils of this world. But Harith was now a prey to wickedness, and had no strength against it; and he came to love and desire the sister for her grace and beauty. When these desires of Harith's became apparent, he knew that he was no longer welcome, and he said to the brother, 'Tomorrow I must bid you both farewell and continue my journey.' And although he said nothing more, both men knew why he felt impelled to go; yet when night fell it seemed as though its black shadow fell upon Harith also, and he crept in the darkness to the brother's tent and killed him sleeping, even as he had killed Khaled. The boy's head he severed with one close stroke of the sword Dhu al Hayat, and thereafter he waited there, tense and silent in the darkness, peering at the severed head; and later in his

'He came upon a brother and his sister living simply'

madness he stabbed the still body with his dagger, but now no blood would run.

Then he entered the tent of the sister and demanded her love, but she would not yield even though he dragged her to her brother's tent and there threatened her. So he had his way by force alone, and in the dim light before dawn he rode from the little camp where the melons grew, and where all had been peace and purity of heart, having violated not only his one true love, but also the basic precepts of this harsh desert world which the tribes have learnt to make their own.

And as he came to Numan's city, he remembered the entreaties of the maiden whose honour he had so cruelly destroyed, and the courtesies of the lad whose hospitality he had so cruelly abused, and for the first time tears of remorse welled in his eyes, and he was torn asunder. For the maiden had opened a new world before his eyes, yet he himself had shut the doors upon its beauty.

At the oasis the maiden, too, wept over her brother's death and her own undoing; and she stabbed herself. And as she lay dying by the waterside, her father came riding to the spring to visit them both; and she whispered the name of the evil man who had shattered all their joy.

Now the old man, her father, sought help from a caravan of merchants who passed by the same road, and between them they buried the lad and his sister, and the old man sought justice against the murderer from Numan, king of Hira. And he travelled swiftly with the merchants, and so it was that when the king and Prince Aswad called Harith before them to discuss the affairs of Abs and Fazara, and the feud with Qais and with 'Antar, the old man cried from the colonnade where he awaited audience with Numan, 'O king, what miracle is this! Lo, I have come to seek justice against a foul murderer who has most cruelly robbed me of my son whom I loved, and my daughter, whom I loved; and who has moreover abused the Arab precepts of hospitality; and see, before ever I make my complaint, you have apprehended him and named him and brought him here to the seat of justice!' And the old man told his dreadful story, and all eyes turned upon Harith as he stood accused on the steps of Numan's throne.

And men came crowding in from the gardens where the fountains played, through the arches of the colonnade, into the great courtyard of Numan's justice. And Harith saw the crowd, and their coloured robes and their brown questioning faces; and he saw the throne and the shadowed arches and the sun beyond shining through the vine leaves; and he heard the fountains playing, and the voice of the old man fell silent. Then King Numan said, 'O Harith, what have you to say in your defence?'

Now it seemed as though all the secret evils of his life blotted out the scene before him, and Harith wept, and in the silence, to the growing horror of the crowds, he began in a quiet voice and as if by rote to list the crimes with which his life was stained; and the people began to murmur, and when he came to tell of the death of the child Shirjibeel, they rose up like a swarm of coloured bees and killed him there in the courts of justice. And no soldier of Numan's moved to save him.

And Harith's blood flowed upon the marble pavement of the colonnade, and not all the fountains of Hira have washed it clean so that, it is said, the stain is visible to this day.

News of this judgement by the people spread far and wide from Numan's kingdom, and came to the ears of the Abs and the Fazara, and this strengthened the peace between them, for their mutual condemnation of Harith was in itself a bond. And Mutajerida could see how wrongly she had acted in releasing this dangerous man, and above all did she regret her betrayal, even if only in thought, of the child Shirjibeel. For she had heard with anguish of the massacre of the Abs children, and this had taught her the value of children, their helpless needs and their innocence. And she came to Numan to beg forgiveness, so that through her repentance their happiness was restored. But King Numan and Prince Aswad could not easily forget their feud with the Abs people, and when Harith was dead they sought a champion to challenge 'Antar. And they found Mugri al Wahash, friend of the wild animals, who alone dared to stand against him.

Now Mugri was a valiant man and a scholar, and when he and his men came south from Syria to the Abs country, Mugri found himself fighting against those he admired and respected, and supported by those he disliked and despised, for Hadifa broke his promises to Qais and joined once more in warfare against the Abs. And battles were waged over many days and weeks, and the fortunes of the Abs people ebbed low. And they were like to be defeated. Yet did 'Antar rouse them in their own defence, and finally Hadifa fell as victim to the sword of Harith ibn Zuhair, he whose love for Labna was become a legend in the tribe. And the Fazara chose new leaders when they heard of the death of Hadifa at the well of Hebat.

Haml also met his death in this battle, and many on both sides of the conflict mourned his passing, for he was a good man.

Then Mugri sent heralds to 'Antar, saying, 'Truly, O leader of the Abs under Lord Qais, enough blood has been shed. Let us now pledge ourselves to fight no more.' And this was agreed. And later Mugri persuaded Prince Aswad and King Numan to consent and ratify a lasting acceptance of the truce, and it became a reality. Moreover, Mugri and 'Antar, who had been enemies, now became friends; and they learned much from each other, the scholar and the poet, talking earnestly night after night in the flickering firelight under the lustrous stars.

Mugri indeed spoke with dignity and knowledge of the ways of gods and men, and when the time came at length for them to part, Mugri revealed that his path lay among those who follow the way of the Prophet Issa, son of Miriam the Virgin. So Mugri left the desert and its people and he dwelt thereafter as a hermit in the church of Bekhran. But some say he later lived near Bosra, on the slopes of the Jebel el Druze as later it came to be called, and that he knew the hermit Bahira. Now it was Bahira who revealed the signs by which mankind could recognize the Prophet (upon whom be peace) when, as a boy, he had journeyed to Syria with merchants from Mecca and was returning home. For Bahira the monk had seen the sign of the cloud and the sign of the tree protecting the boy from the sun's glare, and Bahira saw also the mark between the boy's shoulders and knew that a great personage had come among them.

But this was in the future still, and so, as the caravans pass and pass again across the desert tracks, led by the reliable stars, let us say farewell to the men and women whom we have known so well. To Zuhair and Temadhur, to Harith their son and Labna, to Shedad, and the Prince and Jamila, to Numan and Chosroes and Badramout the Patrician — to Rabia, too, Malec, and his wife Sheriya — and above all to 'Antar, Aboufuwaris, the Knight and virtual leader of his tribe, the poet and lover whom all will remember. Farewell also to 'Abla, with her grace and beauty and wit, her courage and merriment; and to Rabiat, her servant and friend.

And where better can we leave their company, and the memories of those who lived in the memories of these whom we now remember, than at the great feast of reconciliation which Qais and 'Antar held for themselves and for their neighbours, and especially for the Fazara with whom past quarrels had been so bitter? For the feast took place on the slopes of Shereba, where there is both shade and water, and there was much rejoicing and many noble poems were recited to commemorate the peace established both in the north and among the tribes themselves. The feasting lasted many days and nights, and some say that among those who came from afar was an old man whose name will indeed be remembered, Abd al Mutallib of the Hashem tribe from Mecca, he whose descent came from the Quraish, and who spoke to the Abs and the Fazara and all the others assembled, of the year of the Elephant when men from Abyssinia tried to destroy the Ka'aba; and of a boy who was born in that year.

But others say that the great news came to the children of our desert friends, or to their children's children. Yet it is surely known that here among the tribes was this plan worked out and woven in the web of their lives; a plan more marvellous and subtle than anything man could have devised, a plan and a revelation to end the time of the Ignorance. For before many years had passed all became aware not only of the Prophet's youth, and his hidden years — and upon him be peace — but of the two great visions which were to change his life and the lives of thousands thereafter; and soon all could share in the knowledge of the vision of the lote tree shrouded in mystery unspeakable, and of the glorious Being whom the One God sent to speak with Muhammad, blessed be he, high upon the mountainside.